KOREAN ALPHABET
ALPHABET
MADE EASY

*An All-In-One Workbook to Learn How to
Read and Write Hangul [Audio Included]*

Lingo Mastery

ISBN: 978-1-951949-70-9

CONTENTS

INTRODUCTION

Imagine for a moment: you have flown into the Incheon International Airport in South Korea. While looking around, one of the first things you realize might be important is to try and familiarize yourself with the different shapes of Hangul, the Korean Alphabet and understand the pronunciation of each character. Do not be overwhelmed with these strange characters! Most of the signages are written in both Korean and English.

Soon after you start to pay closer attention to these letters, you suddenly begin to grasp how you can read Hangul. Unlike ideograms in the Chinese language where each character represents a particular idea, Hangul characters are phonograms, which means each written symbol stands for a sound like in English. For this reason, it would not be too complicated for an English speaker like you to understand the principles of reading and writing Hangul; it is simple and easy, and you will not easily forget it once you acquire the basic knowledge.

Once you open this book, it will spark your interest in learning to read and write Hangul. As a matter of fact – just a couple of basics will be enough to familiarize yourself with Hangul and the Korean language. Once you grasp the idea, you will be able to sing along to your favorite K-pop lyrics, place an order at a Korean restaurant after reading the names of Korean dishes from the menu and also transcribe your name into Korean. You will, of course, have to learn the vocabulary and grammar later, but having the ability to read and write Hangul can boost your confidence in learning Korean, which will lead you to master it.

This book begins from the very basics, so that even those without any background knowledge about Hangul and Korean can understand it. If you are not a novice learner but have already jumped into learning Korean and want more practice in reading and writing Hangul, coming back to the basics with this book can surely be a good strategy for your long-term study. This book takes gradual steps to expand your understanding, so even after finishing your study, the principles you have learned will remain firm in your memory.

The book pays special attention to the final consonants and the differences among basic, tense and aspirated sounds, which English speakers find most challenging. A sufficient number of exercises as well as audio and visual aids in this book will help you master those points. This book also features key rules of pronunciation when syllables are combined as well as how to read and write single characters. Studying those rules will enable you to sound more natural and fluent even to native speakers.

You have everything you need in front of you and all you have to do now is make the knowledge in this book your own by learning and practicing constantly. Only twenty to thirty minutes a day will help you realize some of the amazing theories of reading and writing in just a few days or weeks at most. One of the favorite proverbs for most Korean people is 'Well begun is half done.' So, congratulations on having already achieved half of your learning, since starting this book is well begun! Now, why don't you complete the other half by studying this book?

PREFACE
ABOUT HANGUL

The Korean alphabet, known as Hangul (also known as Hangeul) in South Korea (Koryo-uh in North Korea), is a writing system for the Korean language created by King Sejong the Great in 1443. The five basic consonants reflect the shape of the speech organs used to pronounce them, and they are systematically modified to indicate phonetic features. The vowels are also systematically modified for related sounds, making Hangul a featural writing system.

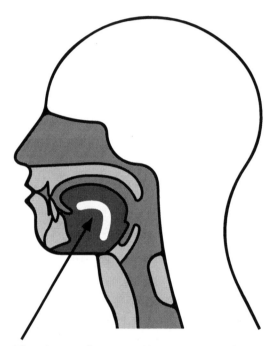

The shape of tongue when pronouncing ㄱ

Modern Hangul orthography uses 24 basic letters: 14 simple consonants (ㄱ,ㄴ,ㄷ,ㄹ,ㅁ,ㅂ,ㅅ,ㅇ,ㅈ,ㅊ,ㅋ, ㅌ,ㅍ,ㅎ) and 10 simple vowels (ㅏ,ㅑ,ㅓ,ㅕ,ㅗ,ㅛ,ㅜ,ㅠ,ㅡ,ㅣ). There are also 27 compound letters formed by combining the simple letters: 5 double consonant letters (ㄲ,ㄸ,ㅃ,ㅆ,ㅉ), 11 compound consonant letters (ㄳ,ㄵ,ㄶ,ㄺ,ㄻ,ㄼ,ㄽ,ㄾ,ㄿ,ㅀ,ㅄ) and 11 compound vowel letters (ㅐ,ㅒ,ㅔ,ㅖ,ㅘ,ㅙ,ㅚ,ㅝ,ㅞ,ㅟ,ㅢ).

Simple Consonants	ㄱ	ㄴ	ㄷ	ㄹ	ㅁ	ㅂ	ㅅ	ㅇ	ㅈ	ㅊ	ㅋ	ㅌ	ㅍ	ㅎ
Simple Vowels	ㅏ	ㅑ	ㅓ	ㅕ	ㅗ	ㅛ	ㅜ	ㅠ	ㅡ	ㅣ				

Double Consonants	ㄲ		ㄸ		ㅃ		ㅆ		ㅉ		
Compound Vowels	ㅐ	ㅒ	ㅔ	ㅖ	ㅘ	ㅙ	ㅚ	ㅝ	ㅞ	ㅟ	ㅢ

Hangul is similar to the English Alphabet, since each letter represents a different sound, but sometimes the letter sound changes depending on the word or the way the word is used. And just like English, Hangul is written from left to right. However, the Korean letters are written in syllabic blocks with the alphabetic letters arranged in two dimensions, which is different from English.

For example, Hangul is spelled in two syllabic blocks, 한글, not in six unarranged letters, ㅎㅏㄴㄱㅡㄹ. These syllabic blocks begin with a consonant letter, then a vowel letter, and then potentially another consonant letter, known as 받침 in Korean, so it follows the CVC structure (Consonant + Vowel + Consonant). If the syllable begins with a vowel sound, then the consonant ㅇ will act as a silent placeholder. However, when ㅇ is placed after a vowel as an ending consonant (받침), it makes the velar nasal sound. The way the syllabic block is arrayed depends on if the vowel is a "tall" vowel (vertical base line) or a "fat" vowel (horizontal base line); if the vowel is "tall" then the first consonant and vowel are written above the second consonant (as in 한, see the picture below), whereas if a vowel is "fat" then all of the components are written individually top to bottom (as in 글, see the picture below).

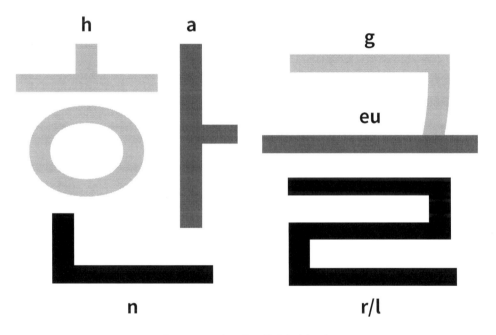

An example of syllable blocks

For convenience, this book uses "romanization" to transcribe Korean phonemes into Roman alphabets. However, it does not exactly correspond to how the characters are pronounced in Korean. Throughout your learning, make sure to focus on the shape of each character and its sound rather than rely entirely on romanization.

HOW TO USE THIS BOOK

This book largely consists of two parts – the first part focuses on how to pronounce and write each Hangul letters properly, whereas the second part introduces some key rules of pronunciation when syllabic blocks are combined as a word.

Each unit in the first part is composed of three gradual steps. At first, it will introduce how each Hangul letter (phoneme) sounds and how it can be written. And then in the second step, you will be given some drills to recognize those letters by listening to audio files or reading example words. Lastly, you will be given some practical exercises where you can read real usages of those letters you learned or dictate what you hear.

The units in the second part also consists of three steps. In the first step, you will learn a pronunciation rule and how it works with examples. Here, you will also practice them by reading along audio files and writing them. Secondly, you will be given some exercises to practice the rule. Thirdly, you will expand your learning to a sentence level by hearing or reading example sentences to which the rule is applied.

A few tips:

> **1.** Each unit introduces various example words or phrases that are commonly used in everyday situations. They are carefully selected considering your future Korean learning and real practice, so please pay close attention to those words and do not just practice how to pronounce or spell the words. It will surely give you a good chance to expand your vocabulary.

> **2.** Please do not read this book only with your eyes, but with your hands and your mouth. Exercises are vital to make the knowledge your own, and you are advised to use all your senses if you want to retain it for a long time. Please do not just try to learn some simple principles by skimming, but also do the exercises for writing and speaking contained in this book. It will not take you too much time.

> **3.** Make good use of blank spaces as much as possible when practicing writing. Please do not write the letters too small. Instead, try to fill in the boxes in the exercises with letters that are big enough, since you cannot recognize or identify the stroke order if you don't write them large enough.

This book is mostly designed to cater to independent studies, but you can also use it in a classroom environment. Whatever situation you are in, it is vital to keep in mind that "Practice makes perfect" and what matters most in learning languages is being constant and not giving it up. Whenever you are experiencing a slump, or you get loose in your study, imagine yourself reading out Korean food names to place an order at a Korean restaurant or writing down some comments in Hangul on the Internet as freely as you want!

HOW TO GET THE AUDIO FILES

Some of the exercises throughout this book come with accompanying audio files.
You can download these audio files if you head over to
www.lingomastery.com/korean-ame-audio

This headphone symbol behind the heading of a text, dialogue or exercise indicates
that audio content is available for the corresponding section.

This headphone with a pencil next to an exercise means that you will need
to refer to the corresponding audio content to complete the exercise.

제 1 장

한글

◇◇◇◇◇◇◇◇◇◇◇◇◇◇◇

CHAPTER 1

HANGUL

제**1**과
모음 I - Vowels I
(ㅏ, ㅓ, ㅗ, ㅜ, ㅡ, ㅣ)

학습목표 OBJECTIVES

✓ How to read and write simple vowels
✓ How to recognize simple vowels in listening and in reading

Part 1

 Below are the simple vowels in Korean. Listen carefully to the recordings and follow them. Each vowel will be read once. (Feel free to play more if you need.) (Find audio on page 5.)

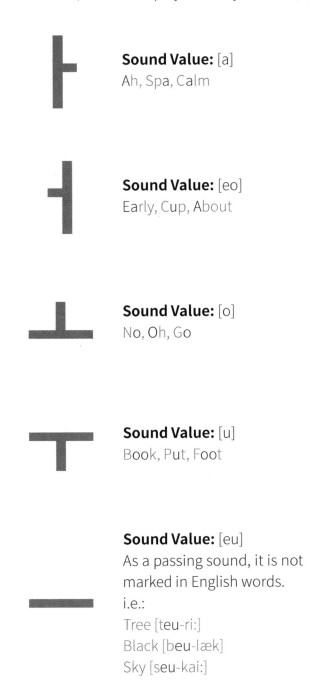

Sound Value: [a]
Ah, Spa, Calm

Sound Value: [eo]
Early, Cup, About

Sound Value: [o]
No, Oh, Go

Sound Value: [u]
Book, Put, Foot

Sound Value: [eu]
As a passing sound, it is not marked in English words.
i.e.:
Tree [teu-ri:]
Black [beu-læk]
Sky [seu-kai:]

Sound Value: [i:]
See, Tea, Kiwi

Let's write each of them, paying attention to the stroke order.

Sound Value: [a]
Ah, Spa, Calm

ㅏ	ㅏ	ㅏ	ㅏ	ㅏ	ㅏ	ㅏ

ㅏ is a vertical vowel, so you should put an initial consonant on the left. When there is no initial consonant, ㅇ is placed as a filler.

아	아	아	아	아	아	아

Pronunciation Tip: ㅏ is an open-back-unrounded vowel. Keep your mouth widely open and produce the sound from the back of your oral cavity.

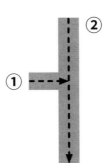

Sound Value: [eo]
Early, Cup, About

ㅓ	ㅓ	ㅓ	ㅓ	ㅓ	ㅓ	ㅓ

ㅓ is a vertical vowel, so you should put an initial consonant on the left. When there is no initial consonant, ㅇ is placed as a filler.

어	어	어	어	어	어	어

Pronunciation Tip: ㅓ is a mid-back-unrounded vowel. Open your mouth (not as widely as ㅏ but still need enough space in between two lips) and produce the sound from the back of your oral cavity.

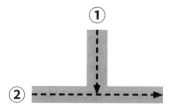

Sound Value: [o]
No, Oh, Go
Not of 'god', 'dog', or 'fox'

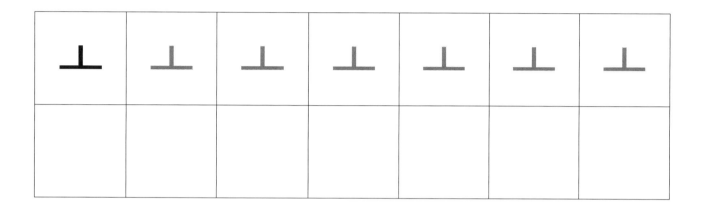

⊥ is a horizontal vowel, so you should put an initial consonant on top of the vowel. When there is no initial consonant, ○ is placed as a filler.

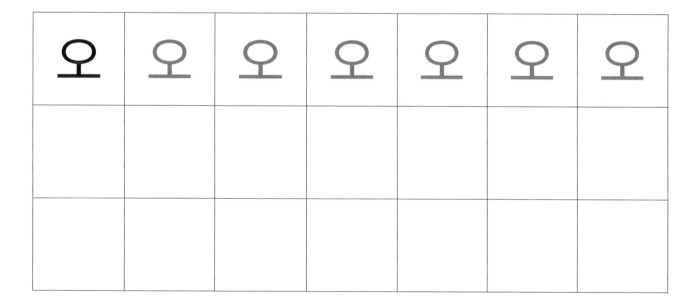

Pronunciation Tip: ⊥ is a mid-back-rounded vowel. Keep enough space in your oral cavity while rounding your lips.

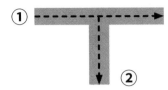

Sound Value: [u]
Book, Put, Foot

ㅜ	ㅜ	ㅜ	ㅜ	ㅜ	ㅜ	ㅜ

ㅜ is a horizontal vowel, so you should put an initial consonant on top of the vowel. When there is no initial consonant, ㅇ is placed as a filler.

우	우	우	우	우	우	우

Pronunciation Tip: ㅜ is a close-back-unrounded vowel. Place your tongue near the palette (higher than ㅗ) and round the lips as if you pout.

Sound Value: [eu]
As a passing sound, it is not
marked in English words.
i.e.:
Tree [teu-ri:]
Black [beu-læk]
Sky [seu-kai:]

①
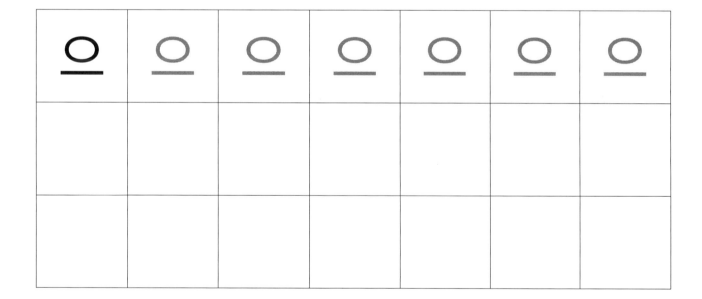

—	—	—	—	—	—	—

— is a horizontal vowel, so you should put an initial consonant on top of the vowel. When there is no initial consonant, ○ is placed as a filler.

으	으	으	으	으	으	으

Pronunciation Tip: — is a closed-back-unrounded vowel. Need to be distinguished from English [eu] sound, your lips should be unrounded and stretched.

Sound Value: [i:]

See, Tea, Kiwi

ㅣ	ㅣ	ㅣ	ㅣ	ㅣ	ㅣ	ㅣ

ㅣ is a vertical vowel, so you should put an initial consonant on the left. When there is no initial consonant, ㅇ is placed as a filler.

이	이	이	이	이	이	이

Pronunciation Tip: ㅣ is a closed-front-unrounded vowel. Pronounce it as if you make English [i] sound.

Part 2

Practice 1

 Listen carefully and choose one that includes the pronunciation of the vowel marked on the left. (Find audio on page 5.)

1. ㅏ   ①   ②

2. ㅓ   ①   ②

3. ㅗ   ①   ②

4. ㅜ   ①   ②

5. ㅡ   ①   ②

6. ㅣ   ①   ②

7. ㅏ   ①   ②   ③

8. ㅓ   ①   ②   ③

9. ㅗ   ①   ②   ③

10. ㅜ   ①   ②   ③

11. ㅡ   ①   ②   ③

12. ㅣ   ①   ②   ③

13. ㅏ   ①   ②   ③   ④

14. ㅓ   ①   ②   ③   ④

15. ㅗ   ①   ②   ③   ④

Practice 2

 Listen carefully and look for the vowel that is pronounced in the given words as shown in the example below. (Multiple answers are possible.) (Find audio on page 5.)

Example

[a] 사랑

1. 노래

2. 우리

3. 아버지

4. 어머니

5. 아저씨

6. 아주머니

7. 자음

8. 모음

9. 봄

10. 여름

11. 가을

12. 겨울

Practice 3

Write down and read the words below.

Cucumber

Child

오	이
오	이

아	이
아	이

Part 3

Practice 1

 Listen carefully to the recordings and write down what you hear. Each one will be read once. (Feel free to play more if you need.) (Find audio on page 5.)

1. _____ .

2. _____ .

3. _____ .

4. _____ .

5. _____ .

6. _____ .

7. _____ .

8. _____ .

9. _____ .

10. _____ .

Practice 2

 Listen carefully to the recordings and circle the vowel that is pronounced. (Find audio on page 5.)

1. 꼬물꼬물

2. 아장아장

3. 엉금엉금

4. 아기자기

5. 요리조리

6. 하늘하늘

7. 우당탕탕

8. 이쪽저쪽

9. 헐렁헐렁

10. 스멀스멀

제 **2** 과
자음 I - Consonants I
(ㄱ, ㄴ, ㄷ, ㄹ, ㅁ)

학습목표 OBJECTIVES

✓ How to read and write five basic consonants

✓ How to recognize five basic consonants in listening and in reading

✓ Learn some words that use simple vowels and five basic consonants

Part 1

 Below are the five basic consonants in Korean. As you can see, consonants have their own alphabet names, which is different from vowels. Listen carefully to the recordings and follow them. Each consonant will be read once. (Feel free to play more if you need.) (Find audio on page 5.)

Alphabet Name: gi-yeok
Sound Value: [g] or [k]
Get, Great, Go

Alphabet Name: ni-eun
Sound Value: [n]
Need, Name, Note

Alphabet Name: di-geut
Sound Value: [d] or [t]
Dog, Drive, Decide

Alphabet Name: ri-eul
Sound Value: [r] or [l]
Right, Light, River

Alphabet Name: mi-eum
Sound Value: [m]
Make, Mind, Meet

Let's write each of them, paying attention to the stroke order.

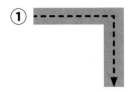

Sound Value: [g] or [k]

기역

Alphabet Name: gi-yeok

Get, Great, Go

ㄱ	ㄱ	ㄱ	ㄱ	ㄱ	ㄱ	ㄱ

Pronunciation Tip: ㄱ is a basic velar sound. Back of your tongue is lifted toward the palette.

Let's combine the consonant with the vowels we learned in the previous unit. Remember to put the initial consonant on the left with a vertical vowel, and on the top with a horizontal vowel. ㄱ can be written with a curve when it's followed by a vertical vowel. (Look 가, 거 and 기) It is not a different consonant but just a style of typography.

가	거	고	구	그	기
가	거	고	구	그	기

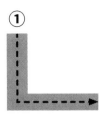

ㄴ

Sound Value: [n]

니은

Alphabet Name: ni-eun

Need, Name, Note

ㄴ	ㄴ	ㄴ	ㄴ	ㄴ	ㄴ	ㄴ

Pronunciation Tip: ㄴ is an alveolar nasal sound. The tip of your tongue touches the upper gum and makes the sound while dropping the tongue and aspirating through the nostrils at the same time.

Let's combine the consonant with the vowels we learned in the previous unit. Remember to put the initial consonant on the left with a vertical vowel, and on the top with a horizontal vowel.

나	너	노	누	느	니
나	너	노	누	느	니

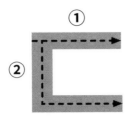

①

②

Sound Value: [d] or [t]

디귿

Alphabet Name: di-geut

Dog, Drive, Decide

ᄃ	ᄃ	ᄃ	ᄃ	ᄃ	ᄃ	ᄃ

Pronunciation Tip: ᄃ is a basic alveolar sound. Place the tip of the tongue at the upper gum and make the sound while detaching the tongue.

Let's combine the consonant with the vowels we learned in the previous unit. Remember to put the initial consonant on the left with a vertical vowel, and on the top with a horizontal vowel.

다	더	도	두	드	디
다	더	도	두	드	디

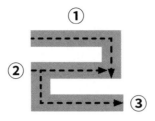

① ② ③

Sound Value: [r] or [l]

리을

Alphabet Name: ri-eul

Right, Light, River

ㄹ	ㄹ	ㄹ	ㄹ	ㄹ	ㄹ	ㄹ

Pronunciation Tip: ㄹ is an alveolar liquid sound. Place the tip of your tongue at the upper gum and make the sound while dropping the tongue downward.

It is still less rhotic than English [r] sound (especially in GA), make sure that you don't roll your tongue too much as if you're pronouncing 'r' at the beginning of the word.

ㄹ is realised as [r] in between two vowels, as if we pronounce t/d in between vowels in GA. (water / butter).

Let's combine the consonant with the vowels we learned in the previous unit. Remember to put the initial consonant on the left with a vertical vowel, and on the top with a horizontal vowel.

라	러	로	루	르	리
라	러	로	루	르	리

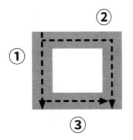

① ② ③

Sound Value: [m]

미음

Alphabet Name: mi-eum

Make, Mind, Meet

ㅁ	ㅁ	ㅁ	ㅁ	ㅁ	ㅁ	ㅁ

Pronunciation Tip: ㅁ is a bilabial nasal sound, close the lips and make the sound while re-opening the mouth.

Let's combine the consonant with the vowels we learned in the previous unit. Remember to put the initial consonant on the left with a vertical vowel, and on the top with a horizontal vowel.

마	머	모	무	므	미
마	머	모	무	므	미

Part 2

Practice 1

 Listen carefully and choose one that includes the pronunciation of the letter marked on the left. (Find audio on page 5.)

1. ㄱ ① ②

2. ㄴ ① ②

3. ㄷ ① ②

4. ㄹ ① ②

5. ㅁ ① ②

6. 기 ① ② ③

7. 다 ① ② ③

8. 머 ① ② ③

9. 노 ① ② ③

10. 루 ① ② ③

11. 그 ① ② ③

12. 니 ① ② ③

13. 라 ① ② ③

14. 더 ① ② ③

15. 모 ① ② ③

Practice 2

 Listen carefully to the recordings and choose the letter that is pronounced. (Find audio on page 5.)

1. 다 / 두 / 디 / 더

2. 고 / 가 / 구 / 그

3. 니 / 나 / 노 / 누

4. 러 / 라 / 리 / 로

5. 므 / 마 / 머 / 무

6. 가 / 기 / 거 / 고

7. 리 / 르 / 루 / 라

8. 무 / 모 / 미 / 마

9. 도 / 드 / 더 / 두

10. 너 / 누 / 나 / 느

11. 구두 / 구더

12. 니라 / 나라

13. 나무 / 나므

14. 도리 / 다리

15. 더리미 / 다리미

16. 라디오 / 라디우

17. 구기 / 고기

18. 노루 / 니루

19. 오리 / 오라

20. 우루 / 우리

Practice 3

Write down and read the words below.

Furniture

Country

ᵏ가ₐ	ᵍ구ᵤ
가	구

ⁿ나ₐ	ʳ라ₐ
나	라

Tree

All

ⁿ나ₐ	ᵐ무ᵤ
나	무

ᵐ모ₒ	ᵈ두ᵤ
모	두

Mother

Radio

어 eo	m 머 eo	n 니 i
어	머	니

r 라 a	d 디 i	오 o
라	디	오

Meat

We

k고o	g기i
고	기

우u	r리i
우	리

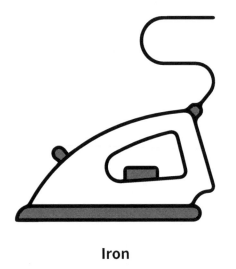

Iron

Duck

d/t다ₐ	r리ᵢ	m미ᵢ
다	리	미

오ₒ	r리ᵢ
오	리

Part 3

Practice 1

Listen carefully to the recordings and write down what you hear. Each one will be read once. (Feel free to play more if you need.) (Find audio on page 5.)

1. _____ .

2. _____ .

3. _____ .

4. _____ .

5. _____ .

6. _____ .

7. _____ .

8. _____ .

9. _____ .

10. _____ .

Practice 2

 Listen carefully to the recordings and circle the consonant that is pronounced.
(Find audio on page 5.)

1. 주사기

2. 하늘

3. 공놀이

4. 꼬리

5. 민들레

6. 만남

7. 도시

8. 가르마

9. 핸드폰

10. 콩고물

제3과

자음 II - Consonants II

(ㅂ,ㅅ,ㅇ,ㅈ,ㅎ)

학습목표 OBJECTIVES

✓ How to read and write five basic consonants

✓ How to recognize five basic consonants in listening and in reading

✓ Learn some words that use simple vowels and five basic consonants

Part 1

Below are the five basic consonants in Korean. As you can see, consonants have their own alphabet names, which is different from vowels. Listen carefully to the recordings and follow them. Each consonant will be read once. (Feel free to play more if you need.) (Find audio on page 5.)

Alphabet Name: bi-eup
Sound Value: [b] or [p]
Baby, Boy, Banana

Alphabet Name: shi-ot
Sound Value: [s] or [sh]
Sand, Set, Shine

Alphabet Name: i-eung
Sound Value: [ng]
Sing, Long, Interesting

Alphabet Name: ji-eut
Sound Value: [j] or [d3]
Join, Joy, Junior

Alphabet Name: hi-eut
Sound Value: [h]
Happy, High, Help

Let's write each of them, paying attention to the stroke order.

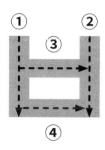

Sound Value: [b] or [p]

비읍

Alphabet Name: bi-eup

Baby, Boy, Banana

ㅂ	ㅂ	ㅂ	ㅂ	ㅂ	ㅂ	ㅂ

Pronunciation Tip: is a bilabial plosive consonant. Close your lips and make the sound while reopening your month and exhaling.

Let's combine the consonant with the vowels we learned. Remember to put the initial consonant on the left with a vertical vowel, and on the top with a horizontal vowel.

바	버	보	부	브	비
바	버	보	부	브	비

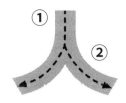

Sound Value: [s] or [sh]

[sh] when it comes with
ㅅ + ㅣ, ㅑ, ㅕ, ㅛ, ㅠ, ㅟ

시옷

Alphabet Name: shi-ot

Sand, Set, Shine

ㅅ	ㅅ	ㅅ	ㅅ	ㅅ	ㅅ	ㅅ

Pronunciation Tip: ㅅ is an alveolar fricative consonant. Place the tip of your tongue near your upper gum and make the sound while leaking air through the gap between your tongue and gum.

Let's combine the consonant with the vowels we learned. Remember to put the initial consonant on the left with a vertical vowel, and on the top with a horizontal vowel.

사	서	소	수	스	시
사	서	소	수	스	시

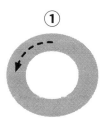

①

Sound Value: None (a filler) as an initial consonant [ng] as a final consonant

이응

Alphabet Name: i-eung

Sing, Long, Interesting

O	O	O	O	O	O	O

Pronunciation Tip: ○ is mute and doesn't make any sound when it's used as a first consonant. Be careful not to get confused with the pronunciation of final ○.

Let's combine the consonant with the vowels we learned. Remember to put the initial consonant on the left with a vertical vowel, and on the top with a horizontal vowel.

아	어	오	우	으	이
아	어	오	우	으	이

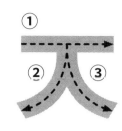

Sound Value: [j] or [d3]

지읒

Alphabet Name: ji-eut

Join, Joy, Junior

ㅈ	ㅈ	ㅈ	ㅈ	ㅈ	ㅈ	ㅈ

Pronunciation Tip: ㅈ is an alveolar-palatal fricative consonant. Place your tongue at the palate (right behind your upper gum) and make a sound while taking your tongue off and exhaling.

Let's combine the consonant with the vowels we learned. Remember to put the initial consonant on the left with a vertical vowel, and on the top with a horizontal vowel. ㅈ can be written both 'ㅈ' and 'ㅈ'. You may choose one form that you find easier to write.

자	저	조	주	즈	지
자	저	조	주	즈	지

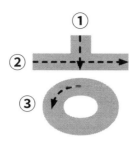

히읗

Alphabet Name: hi-eut

Happy, High, Help

Sound Value: [h]

ㅎ	ㅎ	ㅎ	ㅎ	ㅎ	ㅎ	ㅎ

Pronunciation Tip: ㅎ is a glottal fricative consonant. Make sound while exhaling through your vocal cords.

Let's combine the consonant with the vowels we learned. Remember to put the initial consonant on the left with a vertical vowel, and on the top with a horizontal vowel.

하	허	호	후	흐	히
하	허	호	후	흐	히

Part 2

Practice 1

 Listen carefully and choose one that includes the pronunciation of the letter marked on the left. (Find audio on page 5.)

1. ㅂ ① ②

2. ㅅ ① ②

3. ㅇ ① ②

4. ㅈ ① ②

5. ㅎ ① ②

6. 부 ① ② ③

7. 시 ① ② ③

8. 즈 ① ② ③

9. 호 ① ② ③

10. 어 ① ② ③

11. 버 ① ② ③

12. 수 ① ② ③

13. 즈 ① ② ③

14. 하 ① ② ③

15. 우 ① ② ③

Practice 2

 Listen carefully to the recordings and choose the letter that is pronounced. (Find audio on page 5.)

1. 이 / 아 / 오 / 우

2. 흐 / 히 / 후 / 허

3. 사 / 수 / 서 / 스

4. 바 / 보 / 부 / 비

5. 주 / 자 / 조 / 지

6. 허 / 흐 / 호 / 히

7. 시 / 사 / 소 / 스

8. 우 / 오 / 아 / 으

9. 저 / 조 / 자 / 즈

10. 버 / 부 / 바 / 브

11. 하나 / 하니

12. 지도 / 자두

13. 사조 / 사자

14. 오이 / 오디

15. 바나나 / 버나나

16. 바지 / 바주

17. 모사 / 모자

18. 하라 / 하마

19. 러브 / 리버

20. 보리 / 노리

Practice 3

Write down and read the words below.

Banana

Butterfly

ᵇ바ₐ	ⁿ나ₐ	ⁿ나ₐ
바	나	나

ⁿ나ₐ	ᵇ비ᵢ
나	비

Lion

Seesaw

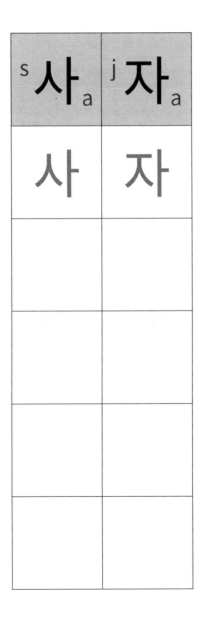

ˢ사ₐ	ʲ자ₐ		ˢ시ᵢ	ˢ소ₒ
사	자		시	소

One

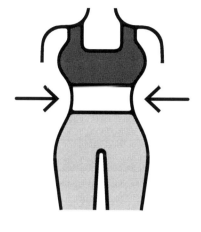

Waist

ʰ하ₐ	ⁿ나ₐ
하	나

ʰ허ₑₒ	ʳ리ᵢ
허	리

Map

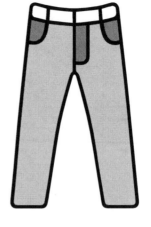

Pants

^j지_i	^d도_o
지	도

^b바_a	^j지_i
바	지

Address

Australia

j 주 u	s 소 o
주	소

h 호 o	j 주 u
호	주

Part 3

Practice 1

 Listen carefully to the recordings and write down what you hear. Each one will be read once. (Feel free to play more if you need.) (Find audio on page 5.)

1. _____ .

2. _____ .

3. _____ .

4. _____ .

5. _____ .

6. _____ .

7. _____ .

8. _____ .

9. _____ .

10. _____ .

Practice 2

 Listen carefully to the recordings and circle the letter(s) you hear from the given sentences. (Find audio on page 5.)

1. 우리 형은 사과를 먹어요.

2. 우리 엄마는 과일을 아주 좋아해요.

3. 누나는 지금 학교에 가요.

4. 어제부터 머리가 아파요.

5. 비가 오면 우비를 입고 외출해요.

6. 하루가 지나면 여행을 가요.

7. 동물원에는 사자가 있어요.

8. 누가 답을 아시나요?

9. 그거 한국말로 뭐예요?

10. 피자에 소스를 뿌려 먹어요.

제4과

모음 II - Vowels II

(ㅑ, ㅕ, ㅛ, ㅠ)

학습목표 OBJECTIVES

✓ How to read and write four simple vowels

✓ How to recognize four simple vowels in listening and in reading

✓ Learn some words that use simple vowels and ten basic consonants

Part 1

 Below are four of the simple vowels in Korean. The short extra strokes signify the additional /i/ sound before the original vowel sound. Listen carefully to the recordings and follow them. Each vowel will be read once. (Feel free to play more if you need.)

Sound Value: [ya]
Yahoo, Papaya

Sound Value: [yeo]
Young, Year

Sound Value: [yo]
Mayonnaise, Yoga

Sound Value: [yu]
Youth, You

Let's write each of them, paying attention to the stroke order.

Sound Value: [ya]
Yahoo, Papaya

ㅑ	ㅑ	ㅑ	ㅑ	ㅑ	ㅑ	ㅑ

Pronunciation Tip: compare ㅏ and ㅑ (/i/+ ㅏ) carefully.

Let's combine ㅑ with the consonants we learned in the previous units. Remember to put the initial consonants on the left, as ㅑ is a vertical vowel.

갸	갸				
냐	냐				
댜	댜				
랴	랴				
먀	먀				
뱌	뱌				
샤	샤				
야	야				
쟈	쟈				
햐	햐				

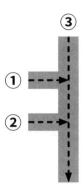

Sound Value: [yeo]

Young, Year

ㅕ	ㅕ	ㅕ	ㅕ	ㅕ	ㅕ	ㅕ

Pronunciation Tip: compare ㅓ and ㅕ (/i/+ ㅓ) carefully.

Let's combine ㅕ with the consonants we learned in the previous units. Remember to put the initial consonants on the left, as ㅕ is a vertical vowel.

겨	겨				
녀	녀				
뎌	뎌				
려	려				
며	며				
벼	벼				
셔	셔				
여	여				
져	져				
혀	혀				

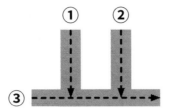

Sound Value: [yo]

Mayonnaise, Yoga

ㅛ	ㅛ	ㅛ	ㅛ	ㅛ	ㅛ	ㅛ

Pronunciation Tip: compare ㅗ and ㅛ (/i/+ㅛ) carefully.

Let's combine ㅛ with the consonants we learned in the previous units. Remember to put the initial consonants on the top, as ㅛ is a horizontal vowel.

교	교				
뇨	뇨				
됴	됴				
료	료				
묘	묘				
뵤	뵤				
쇼	쇼				
요	요				
죠	죠				
효	효				

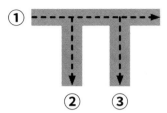

Sound Value: [yu]
Youth, You

ㅠ	ㅠ	ㅠ	ㅠ	ㅠ	ㅠ	ㅠ

Pronunciation Tip: compare ㅜ and ㅠ (/i/+ㅜ) carefully.

Let's combine ㅠ with the consonants we learned in the previous units. Remember to put the initial consonants on the top, as ㅠ is a horizontal vowel.

규	규				
뉴	뉴				
듀	듀				
류	류				
뮤	뮤				
뷰	뷰				
슈	슈				
유	유				
쥬	쥬				
휴	휴				

Part 2

Practice 1

 Listen carefully and choose one that includes the pronunciation of the letter marked on the left.

1. ㅑ ① ②

2. ㅓ ① ②

3. ㅛ ① ②

4. ㅠ ① ②

5. 효 ① ② ③

6. 벼 ① ② ③

7. 쟈 ① ② ③

8. 슈 ① ② ③

9. 묘 ① ② ③

10. 야 ① ② ③

11. 뷰 ① ② ③

12. 녀 ① ② ③

13. 샤 ① ② ③

14. 교 ① ② ③

15. 휴 ① ② ③

Practice 2

 Listen carefully to the recordings and choose the letter that is pronounced.

1. 쇼 / 소 / 슈 / 수

2. 냐 / 너 / 누 / 뇨

3. 류 / 라 / 료 / 로

4. 조 / 죠 / 주 / 쥬

5. 미 / 먀 / 묘 / 모

6. 버 / 보 / 뱌 / 벼

7. 가 / 갸 / 거 / 겨

8. 됴 / 도 / 더 / 드

9. 야 / 여 / 으 / 이

10. 혀 / 하 / 흐 / 휴

11. 여자 / 야자

12. 유유 / 우유

13. 요자 / 효자

14. 묘지 / 모지

15. 유리 / 유미

16. 보기 / 뵤기

17. 우리 / 요리

18. 소녀 / 소냐

19. 교려 / 고려

20. 조류 / 조리

Practice 3

Change the English transcriptions into Hangul as shown in the example. The definitions of the words are given in brackets.

Example

Yeo-ja (woman) → **여자**

1. Yu-ri (glass)

_____.

2. Do-gu (tool)

_____.

3. Ya-ja-su (palm tree)

_____.

4. Ba-gu-ni (basket)

_____.

5. Gi-reo-gi (wild goose)

_____.

6. Ho-mi (hoe)

_____.

7. Ji-gu (the Earth)

_____.

8. Neo-gu-ri (raccoon)

_____.

9. Ho-du (walnut)

_____.

10. Ba-da (sea)

_____.

11. Beo-s (bus)

_____.

12. Mo-gi (mosquito)

_____.

13. Geo-ri (street)

_____.

14. Gyeo-ja (mustard)

_____.

15. Sa-i-da (soda drink)

_____.

16. Myo-ji (cemetery)

_____.

17. Du-yu (soy milk)

_____.

18. Ja-yu (freedom)

_____.

19. Gyo-su (professor)

_____.

20. Ya-gu (baseball)

_____.

Practice 4

Write down and read the words below.

Tongue

Rice (In Stalks)

Food, Cooking

Milk

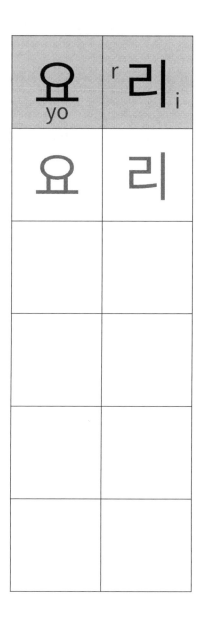

요 yo	ʳ 리 ᵢ	우 u	유 yu
요	리	우	유

News

Story, Talking

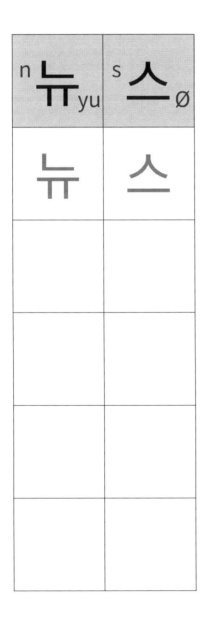

ⁿ뉴yu	ˢ스∅
뉴	스

이ᵢ	야ya	ᵍ기ᵢ
이	야	기

Girl

Condiment

s소o	n녀yeo
소	녀

j조o	m미i	r료yo
조	미	료

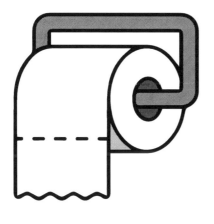

Toilet Paper

Gas Station

ʰ휴yu	ʲ지i
휴	지

ʲ주u	유yu	ˢ소o
주	유	소

Part 3

Practice 1

Listen carefully to the recordings and write down what you hear. Each one will be read once. (Feel free to play more if you need.)

1. _____ .

2. _____ .

3. _____ .

4. _____ .

5. _____ .

6. _____ .

7. _____ .

8. _____ .

9. _____ .

10. _____ .

11. _____ .

12. _____ .

13. _____ .

14. _____ .

15. _____ .

16. _____ .

17. _____ .

18. _____ .

19. _____ .

20. _____ .

Practice 2

 Listen carefully to the recordings and circle the letter(s) you hear from the given sentences.

1. 인터넷에서 자료를 검색해요.

2. 이유를 모르겠어요.

3. 그것은 명백한 루머예요.

4. 방탄소년단에 대한 뉴스를 들었어요?

5. 영화 미나리가 아카데미상을 받았어요!

6. 당분간 이 영화는 무료로 볼 수 있어요.

7. 저는 아이스 아메리카노 한 잔 주세요.

8. 일곱 시 삼십 분에 거기에서 뵐게요.

9. 자동차로 가는 게 지하철로 가는 것보다 느려요.

10. 지금 저는 주머니에 카드 밖에 없어요.

제5과

자음 III - Consonants III

(ㅋ, ㅌ, ㅍ, ㅊ)

학습목표 OBJECTIVES

✓ How to read and write four aspirated sound consonants

✓ How to recognize four aspirated sound consonants in listening and in reading

✓ Learn some words that use simple vowels and four aspirated sound consonants

Part 1

 Below are four aspirated sound consonants in Korean. Listen carefully to the recordings and follow them. Each consonant will be read once. (Feel free to play more if you need.)

 Alphabet Name: ki-euk
Sound Value: [k] or [kʰ]
King, Kick, Korea

 Alphabet Name: ti-eut
Sound Value: [t] or [tʰ]
Take, Table, Tea

 Alphabet Name: pi-eup
Sound Value: [p] or [pʰ]
Positive, Place, Paint

 Alphabet Name: chi-eut
Sound Value: [ch] or [tʃʰ]
Chair, Charge, Choose

Let's write each of them, paying attention to the stroke order.

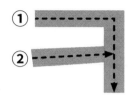

Sound Value: [k] or [kʰ]

키읔

Alphabet Name: ki-euk

King, Kick, Korea

ㅋ	ㅋ	ㅋ	ㅋ	ㅋ	ㅋ	ㅋ

Pronunciation Tip: compare ㄱ and ㅋ (ㄱ with aspiration) carefully.

Let's combine the consonant with the vowels we learned. Remember to put the initial consonant on the left with a vertical vowel, and on the top with a horizontal vowel.

카	커	코	쿠	크	키
카	커	코	쿠	크	키

캬	켜	쿄	큐
캬	켜	쿄	큐

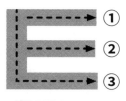

Sound Value: [t] or [tʰ]

Alphabet Name: ti-eut

Take, Table, Tea

ㅌ	ㅌ	ㅌ	ㅌ	ㅌ	ㅌ

Pronunciation Tip: compare ㄷ and ㅌ (ㄷ with aspiration) carefully.

Let's combine the consonant with the vowels we learned. Remember to put the initial consonant on the left with a vertical vowel, and on the top with a horizontal vowel.

타	터	토	투	트	티
타	터	토	투	트	티

탸	텨	툐	튜
탸	텨	툐	튜

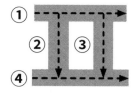

Sound Value: [p] or [pʰ]

피읖

Alphabet Name: pi-eup

Positive, Place, Paint

ㅍ	ㅍ	ㅍ	ㅍ	ㅍ	ㅍ	ㅍ

Pronunciation Tip: compare ㅂ and ㅍ (ㅂ with aspiration) carefully.

Let's combine the consonant with the vowels we learned. Remember to put the initial consonant on the left with a vertical vowel, and on the top with a horizontal vowel.

파	퍼	포	푸	프	피
파	퍼	포	푸	프	피

퍄	펴	표	퓨
퍄	펴	표	퓨

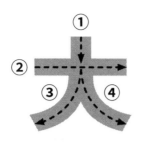

Sound Value: [ch] or [t ʃʰ]

치읓

Alphabet Name: chi-eut
Chair, Charge, Choose

大	大	大	大	大	大	大

Pronunciation Tip: compare ㅈ and ㅊ (ㅈ with aspiration) carefully.

Let's combine the consonant with the vowels we learned. Remember to put the initial consonant on the left with a vertical vowel, and on the top with a horizontal vowel.

차	처	초	추	츠	치
차	처	초	추	츠	치

챠	쳐	쵸	츄
챠	쳐	쵸	츄

Part 2

Practice 1

 Listen carefully and choose one that includes the pronunciation of the letter marked on the left.

1. ㅋ ① ②

2. ㅌ ① ②

3. ㅍ ① ②

4. ㅊ ① ②

5. 카 ① ② ③

6. 토 ① ② ③

7. 피 ① ② ③

8. 추 ① ② ③

9. 퓨 ① ② ③

10. 커 ① ② ③

11. 트 ① ② ③

12. 차 ① ② ③

13. 표 ① ② ③

14. 쿠 ① ② ③

15. 터 ① ② ③

Practice 2

 Listen carefully to the recordings and choose the letter that is pronounced.

1. 카 / 타

2. 츠 / 프

3. 코 / 포

4. 퍼 / 터

5. 키 / 치

6. 추 / 투

7. 가 / 카

8. 다 / 타

9. 바 / 파

10. 자 / 차

11. 고 / 코

12. 도 / 토

13. 보 / 포

14. 조 / 초

15. 규 / 큐

16. 듀 / 튜

17. 뷰 / 퓨

18. 쥬 / 츄

19. 교 / 쿄

20. 됴 / 툐

21. 뵤 / 표

22. 죠 / 쵸

23. 기 / 키

24. 디 / 티

25. 비 / 피

26. 지 / 치

27. 그 / 크

28. 드 / 트

29. 브 / 프

30. 즈 / 츠

Practice 3

 Listen carefully to the recordings and fill in the missing letters of the given words.

1. ☐ 지

2. ☐ 무

3. ☐ 시

4. 도 ☐ 리

5. ☐ 지

6. ☐ 마

7. ☐ 다

8. ☐ 도

9. 코 ☐

10. ☐ 조

11. ☐ 즈

12. ☐ 도

13. ☐ 자마

14. ☐ 자

Practice 4

Change the English transcriptions into Hangul as shown in the example. The definitions of the words are given in brackets.

> **Example**
> Chi-ma (skirt) → 치마

1. Cha-pyo (transportation ticket)

_____.

2. Ja-du (plum)

_____.

3. Pyo-si (mark, indication)

_____.

4. Mo-ni-teo (monitor)

_____.

5. Du-deo-ji (mole)

_____.

6. Pa-do (wave)

_____.

7. Ba-i-reo-s (virus)

_____.

8. Ba-ri-s-ta (barista)

_____.

9. To-ma-to (tomato)

_____.

10. Do-ma (cutting board)

_____.

11. To-s-t (toasted bread)

_____.

12. Do-ra-ji (balloon flower root)

_____.

13. A-pa-t (apartment)

_____.

14. Gyu-mo (size, scale)

_____.

15. S-ti-keo (sticker)

_____.

16. Geo-mi (spider)

_____.

17. Ma-s-k (mask)

_____.

18. G-nyeo (she)

_____.

19. Ta-jo (ostrich)

_____.

20. Ba-da (sea)

_____.

Practice 5

Write down and read the words below.

Coffee

Cookie

ᵏ커ₑₒ	ᵖ피ᵢ
커	피

ᵏ쿠ᵤ	ᵏ키ᵢ
쿠	키

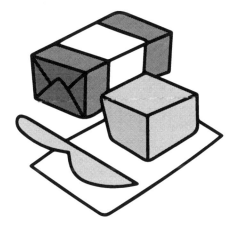

Butter

Pizza

ᵇ버ₑₒ	ᵗ터ₑₒ		ᵖ피ᵢ	ʲ자ₐ
버	터		피	자

Coat

T-Shirt

k 코 o	t 트 ø
코	트

t 티 i	sh 셔 yeo	ch 츠 ø
티	셔	츠

Postage Stamp

Card

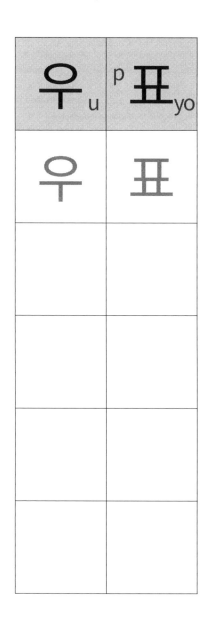

우 u	p 표 yo
우	표

k 카 a	d 드 ø
카	드

Chocolate

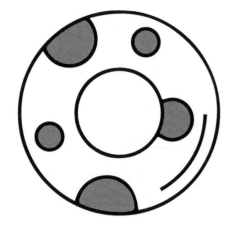

Tube

ch초ₒ	k코ₒ
초	코

t튜yu	b브∅
튜	브

Grapes

Acorn

p포o	d도o
포	도

d도o	t토o	r리i
도	토	리

Part 3

Practice 1

 Listen carefully to the recordings and write down what you hear. Each one will be read once. (Feel free to play more if you need.)

1. _____ .

2. _____ .

3. _____ .

4. _____ .

5. _____ .

6. _____ .

7. _____ .

8. _____ .

9. _____ .

10. _____ .

11. _____ .

12. _____ .

13. _____ .

14. _____ .

15. _____ .

16. _____ .

17. _____ .

18. _____ .

19. _____ .

20. _____ .

Practice 2

 Listen carefully to the recordings and circle the letter(s) you hear from the given sentences.

1. 우리 커피 한 잔 하실까요?

2. 튜브가 없으면 물놀이를 못해요.

3. 고구마 피자하고 콜라 한 잔 주세요.

4. 저는 빵에 버터대신 치즈를 발라서 먹어요.

5. 가을에는 산에 가면 도토리를 많이 주울 수 있어요.

6. 이제 날씨가 쌀쌀해졌으니까 코트를 꺼내야겠어요.

7. 이 티셔츠는 가격이 얼마예요?

8. 지금 현금은 없고 카드가 있어요.

9. 아침마다 토마토 주스를 한 잔씩 마셔요.

10. 바이러스를 막으려면 손을 잘 씻어야 해요.

11. 오토바이 타 본 적 있으세요?

12. 그녀는 치마보다 바지를 좋아해요.

13. 토스트 한 개에 우유 한 잔을 마셔요.

14. 우리 같이 바비큐 먹으러 가요.

15. 실내에서는 마스크를 착용해 주세요.

제6과

자음 IV - Consonants IV

(ㄲ,ㄸ,ㅃ,ㅆ,ㅉ)

학습목표 OBJECTIVES

✓ How to read and write five tense sound consonants

✓ How to recognize five tense sound consonants in listening and in reading

✓ Learn some words that use simple vowels and five tense sound consonants

✓ How to differentiate tense sounds from aspirated sounds and lax sounds

Part 1

 Below are five tense sound consonants in Korean. Listen carefully to the recordings and follow them. Each consonant will be read once. (Feel free to play more if you need.)

 Alphabet Name: ssang-gi-yeok
Sound Value: [kk] or [k']

 Alphabet Name: ssang-di-geut
Sound Value: [tt] or [t']

 Alphabet Name: ssang-bi-eup
Sound Value: [pp] or [p']

 Alphabet Name: ssang-shi-ot
Sound Value: [ss] or [s']

 Alphabet Name: ssang-ji-eut
Sound Value: [jj] or [t ʃ']

As you might have already noticed, there are three different categories in Korean consonants; lax sounds, tense sounds and aspirated sounds. The table below shows the system.

Lax	Tense	Aspirated
ㄱ	ㄲ	ㅋ
ㄷ	ㄸ	ㅌ
ㅂ	ㅃ	ㅍ
ㅅ	ㅆ	-
ㅈ	ㅉ	ㅊ

The three kinds could sound very similar or nearly the same to English speakers, since those sounds are marked or regarded same. However, the distinction among those three is so clear in the Korean language that it can even have influence on the meanings of the words. So, try to find out the subtle differences among them while listening to the recordings in the exercises!

Let's practice reading and writing each of them. Listen carefully to the recordings and follow them, trying to figure out the differences. Then, practice writing with the right stroke order.

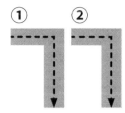

쌍기역

Alphabet Name: ssang-gi-yeok
Sound Value: [kk] or [k']

가	까	카
거	꺼	커
고	꼬	코
구	꾸	쿠
그	끄	크
기	끼	키

까	까					
꺼	꺼					
꼬	꼬					
꾸	꾸					
끄	끄					
끼	끼					
꺄	꺄					
껴	껴					
꾜	꾜					
뀨	뀨					

	ㅏ	ㅓ	ㅗ	ㅜ	ㅡ	ㅣ
ㄱ	가					
ㄲ	까					
ㅋ	카					

	ㅑ	ㅕ	ㅛ	ㅠ
ㄱ	갸			
ㄲ	까			
ㅋ	캬			

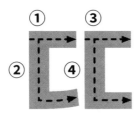

쌍디귿

Alphabet Name: ssang-di-geut
Sound Value: [tt] or [t']
Never used as a final consonant

다	따	타
더	떠	터
도	또	토
두	뚜	투
드	뜨	트
디	띠	티

Pronunciation Tip: compare ㄷ and ㄸ carefully. When pronouncing ㄸ, your tongue pushes the upper teeth harder than when you make ㄷ sound.

Let's practice writing!

따	따					
떠	떠					
또	또					
뚜	뚜					
뜨	뜨					
띠	띠					
땨	땨					
뗘	뗘					
뚀	뚀					
뜌	뜌					

	ㅏ	ㅓ	ㅗ	ㅜ	ㅡ	ㅣ
ㄷ	다					
ㄸ	따					
ㅌ	타					

	ㅑ	ㅕ	ㅛ	ㅠ
ㄷ	댜			
ㄸ	땨			
ㅌ	탸			

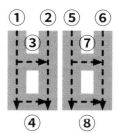

쌍비읍

Alphabet Name: ssang-bi-eup
Sound Value: [pp] or [p']
Never used as a final consonant

바	빠	파
버	뻐	퍼
보	뽀	포
부	뿌	푸
브	쁘	프
비	삐	피

Pronunciation Tip: compare ㅂ and ㅃ carefully. When pronouncing ㅃ, your lips are closed firmer and more stiffened than when you make ㅂ sound.

빠	빠					
뻐	뻐					
뽀	뽀					
뿌	뿌					
쁘	쁘					
삐	삐					
빠	빠					
뻐	뻐					
뽀	뽀					
뿌	뿌					

	ㅏ	ㅓ	ㅗ	ㅜ	ㅡ	ㅣ
ㅂ	바					
ㅃ	빠					
ㅍ	파					

	ㅑ	ㅕ	ㅛ	ㅠ
ㅂ	뱌			
ㅃ	뺘			
ㅍ	퍄			

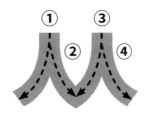

쌍시옷

Alphabet Name: ssang-shi-ot
Sound Value: [ss] or [s']

사	싸
서	써
소	쏘
수	쑤
스	쓰
시	씨

Pronunciation Tip: compare ㅅ and ㅆ carefully. When pronouncing ㅆ, your tongue is more stiffened and you aspirate stronger air than when you make ㅅ sound.

Let's practice writing!

싸	싸					
써	써					
쏘	쏘					
쑤	쑤					
쓰	쓰					
씨	씨					
쌰	쌰					
쎠	쎠					
쑈	쑈					
쓔	쓔					

	ㅏ	ㅓ	ㅗ	ㅜ	ㅡ	ㅣ
ㅅ	사					
ㅆ	싸					

	ㅑ	ㅕ	ㅛ	ㅠ
ㅅ	샤			
ㅆ	쌰			

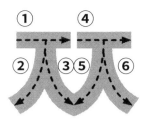

쌍지읒

Alphabet Name: ssang-ji-eut
Sound Value: [jj] or [tʃ']

자	짜	차
저	쩌	처
조	쪼	초
주	쭈	추
즈	쯔	츠
지	찌	치

Pronunciation Tip: compare ㅈ and ㅉ carefully. When pronouncing ㅉ, your tongue pushes the upper gum harder than when you make ㅈ sound.

Let's practice writing!

짜	짜					
쩌	쩌					
쪼	쪼					
쭈	쭈					
쯔	쯔					
찌	찌					
쨔	쨔					
쪄	쪄					
쬬	쬬					
쮸	쮸					

	ㅏ	ㅓ	ㅗ	ㅜ	ㅡ	ㅣ
ㅈ	자					
ㅉ	짜					
ㅊ	차					

	ㅑ	ㅕ	ㅛ	ㅠ
ㅈ	쟈			
ㅉ	쨔			
ㅊ	챠			

Part 2

Practice 1

 Listen carefully and choose one that includes the pronunciation of the letter marked on the left.

1. ㄲ ① ② ③

2. ㄸ ① ② ③

3. ㅃ ① ② ③

4. ㅆ ① ② ③

5. ㅉ ① ② ③

6. 빠 ① ② ③

7. 또 ① ② ③

8. 쮸 ① ② ③

9. 꼬 ① ② ③

10. 쏘 ① ② ③

11. 부 ① ② ③

12. 디 ① ② ③

13. 처 ① ② ③

14. 교 ① ② ③

15. 토 ① ② ③

Practice 2

 Listen carefully to the recordings and choose the letter that is pronounced.

1. 가 / 카

2. 꼬 / 고

3. 처 / 저

4. 쨔 / 쟈

5. 시 / 씨

6. 죠 / 쪼

7. 껴 / 켜

8. 투 / 뚜

9. 뽀 / 보

10. 쳐 / 쪄

11. 더 / 터

12. 샤 / 쌰

13. 주 / 추

14. 뜨 / 드

15. 꾸 / 쿠

16. 버 / 퍼

17. 뎌 / 텨

18. 쓰 / 스

19. 치 / 찌

20. 꺼 / 커

Practice 3

 Listen carefully to the recordings and fill in the missing letters of the given words.

1. 까 ▢

2. 가 ▢

3. ▢ 리

4. ▢ 리

5. ▢ 끼리

6. ▢ 리

7. 아 ▢ 지

8. 아 ▢

9. ▢ 르르

10. ▢ 르마

11. ▢ 브 ▢ 브

12. 으 ▢ 으 ▢

Practice 4

Read out loud the words below, paying attention to the differences of lax sounds, tense sounds, and aspirated sounds.

1. 우리 아빠가 거기로 가요.

2. 피노키오가 아파요.

3. 꼬치도 사고 피자도 사요.

4. 지도 보고 아프리카로 가요.

5. 아파트가 아주 커요.

6. 마스크 쓰고 슈퍼로 가요.

7. 허수아비가 코스모스를 바라봐요.

8. 어서 자라라.

9. 여기 나무 뿌리가 커요.

10. 저 오토바이가 빠르다.

Practice 5

Write down and read the words below.

Dad

Middle-Aged Man

아 _a	^{pp}빠 _a
아	빠

아 _a	^j저 _{eo}	^{ss}씨 _i
아	저	씨

Rabbit

Elephant

ᵗ토 ₒ	ᵏᵏ끼 ᵢ
토	끼

ᵏ코 ₒ	ᵏᵏ끼 ᵢ	ʳ리 ᵢ
코	끼	리

Fake

To Argue, To Fight

ᵍ가ₐ	ʲʲ짜ₐ
가	짜

ˢˢ싸ₐ	우ᵤ	ᵈ다ₐ
싸	우	다

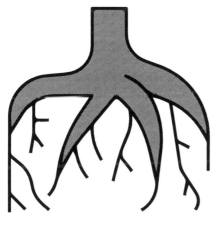

Root

Belt

pp뿌u	r리i
뿌	리

h허eo	r리i	tt띠i
허	리	띠

To Pour

To Pierce, To Poke

tt따a	r르ø	d다a
따	르	다

jj찌i	r르ø	d다a
찌	르	다

Part 3

Practice 1

Listen carefully to the recordings and write down what you hear. Each one will be read once. (Feel free to play more if you need.)

1. _____.

2. _____.

3. _____.

4. _____.

5. _____.

6. _____.

7. _____.

8. _____.

9. _____.

10. _____.

11. _____.

12. _____.

13. _____.

14. _____.

15. _____.

16. _____.

17. _____.

18. _____.

19. _____.

20. _____.

Practice 2

 Listen carefully to the recordings and circle the letter(s) you hear from the given sentences.

1. 강아지 꼬리가 귀여워요.

2. 자전거보다 자동차가 빠르다.

3. 지하철은 생각보다 많이 느려요.

4. 오늘 저녁은 두부찌개를 먹도록 해요.

5. 그 사람은 이번에도 또 늦었어요?

6. 오프라인보다 인터넷이 더 싸다.

7. 아빠는 오늘도 늦으니까 저녁 먼저 먹어요.

8. 물을 너무 많이 줘서 뿌리가 다 썩었다.

9. 새의 부리가 너무 날카로워요.

10. 엄마, 국이 너무 짜요.

11. 여름에는 해가 아침 일찍 떠요.

12. 손님의 잔에 물을 따르다.

13. 이 도자기는 조선 시대에 만들어졌어요.

14. 세수하기 전에 머리띠를 해야 해요.

15. 이 사람은 아저씨가 아니라 오빠다.

제 **7** 과

모음 III – Vowels III

(ㅐ,ㅔ,ㅒ,ㅖ,ㅘ,ㅝ)

학습목표 OBJECTIVES

✓ How to read and write six compound vowels

✓ How to recognize six compound vowels in listening and in reading

✓ Learn some words that use different kinds of vowels and six compound vowels

Part 1

 Below are the six compound vowels in Korean. Listen carefully to the recordings and follow them. Each vowel will be read once. (Feel free to play more if you need.)

Sound Value: [æ]
Apple, Cat, Bag

Current speakers of Standard Korean do not differentiate between the vowels ㅐ and ㅔ in pronunciation.

Sound Value: [e]
Bed, Set, Pen

Current speakers of Standard Korean do not differentiate between the vowels ㅐ and ㅔ in pronunciation.

Sound Value: [yɛ] or [ye]
Yes, Yellow, Yet

Current speakers of Standard Korean do not differentiate between the vowels ㅒ and ㅖ in pronunciation.

Sound Value: [yɛ] or [ye]
Yes, Yellow, Yet

Current speakers of Standard Korean do not differentiate between the vowels ㅒ and ㅖ in pronunciation.

Sound Value: [wa]
Wow, What, Watch

Sound Value: [wə]
Want, Worry, Water

Let's write each of them, paying attention to the stroke order.

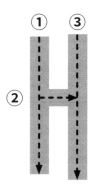

Sound Value: [æ]
Apple, Cat, Bag

Current speakers of Standard Korean do not differentiate between the vowels ㅐ and ㅔ in pronunciation.

ㅐ	ㅐ	ㅐ	ㅐ	ㅐ	ㅐ	ㅐ

Pronunciation Tip: ㅐ is an open vowel. Lower your tongue and make the sound while opening widely your lips.

Let's combine ㅐ with the consonants we learned in the previous units. Remember to put the initial consonants on the left, as ㅐ is a vertical vowel.

개	개				
내	내				
대	대				
래	래				
매	매				
배	배				
새	새				
애	애				
재	재				
해	해				

캐	캐				
태	태				
패	패				
채	채				
깨	깨				
때	때				
빼	빼				
쌔	쌔				
째	째				

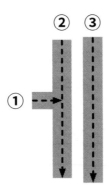

Sound Value: [e]

Bed, Set, Pen

Current speakers of Standard Korean
do not differentiate between the vowels
ㅐ and ㅔ in pronunciation.

ㅔ	ㅔ	ㅔ	ㅔ	ㅔ	ㅔ	ㅔ

Pronunciation Tip: ㅔ is more closed compared to ㅐ, even though in modern
pronunciation it is barely distinguishable.

Let's combine ㅔ with the consonants we learned in the previous units. Remember to put the initial consonants on the left, as ㅔ is a vertical vowel.

게	게				
네	네				
데	데				
레	레				
메	메				
베	베				
세	세				
에	에				
제	제				
헤	헤				

케	케				
테	테				
페	페				
체	체				
께	께				
떼	떼				
뻬	뻬				
쎄	쎄				
쩨	쩨				

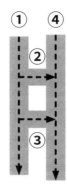

① ④
② ③

이**애**

Sound Value: [yɛ] or [ye]
Yes, Yellow, Yet

To pronounce ㅒ correctly, you can start pronouncing ㅣ first, and then slide to pronouncing ㅐ. ㅣ should be shorter than ㅐ.

Current speakers of Standard Korean do not differentiate between the vowels ㅒ and ㅖ in pronunciation.

ㅒ	ㅒ	ㅒ	ㅒ	ㅒ	ㅒ	ㅒ

Let's combine ㅐ with the consonants we learned in the previous units. Remember to put the initial consonants on the left, as ㅐ is a vertical vowel.

걔	걔				
냬	냬				
댸	댸				
럐	럐				
먜	먜				
뱨	뱨				
섀	섀				
얘	얘				
쟤	쟤				
햬	햬				

캐	캐				
태	태				
패	패				
채	채				
깨	깨				
때	때				
빼	빼				
쌔	쌔				
째	째				

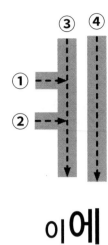

이예

Sound Value: [yɛ] or [ye]
Yes, Yellow, Yet

To pronounce ᅨ correctly, you can start pronouncing ㅣ first, and then slide to pronouncing ᅦ. ㅣ should be shorter than ᅦ.

Current speakers of Standard Korean do not differentiate between the vowels ᅤ and ᅨ in pronunciation.

ᅨ	ᅨ	ᅨ	ᅨ	ᅨ	ᅨ	ᅨ

Let's combine ㅖ with the consonants we learned in the previous units. Remember to put the initial consonants on the left, as ㅖ is a vertical vowel.

계	계				
녜	녜				
뎨	뎨				
례	례				
몌	몌				
볘	볘				
셰	셰				
예	예				
졔	졔				
혜	혜				

켸	켸				
톄	톄				
폐	폐				
쳬	쳬				
꼐	꼐				
뗴	뗴				
뼤	뼤				
쎼	쎼				
쪠	쪠				

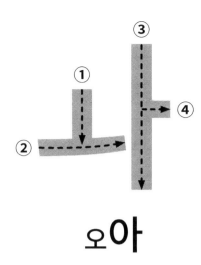

오아

Sound Value: [wa]
Wow, What, Watch

To pronounce ㅘ correctly, you can start pronouncing ㅗ first, and then slide to pronouncing ㅏ. ㅗ should be shorter than ㅏ.

과	과	과	과	과	과	과

Let's combine ㅘ with the consonants we learned in the previous units. Remember to put the initial consonants on the upper-left, as ㅘ is a combination of a horizontal vowel ㅗ and a vertical vowel ㅏ.

과	과				
놔	놔				
돠	돠				
롸	롸				
뫄	뫄				
봐	봐				
솨	솨				
와	와				
좌	좌				
화	화				

콰	콰				
톼	톼				
퐈	퐈				
촤	촤				
꽈	꽈				
똬	똬				
뽜	뽜				
쏴	쏴				
쫘	쫘				

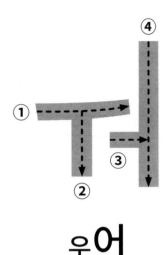

Sound Value: [wə]

Want, Worry, Water

To pronounce ㅝ correctly, you can start pronouncing ㅜ first, and then slide to pronouncing ㅓ. ㅜ should be shorter than ㅓ.

우어

ㅝ	ㅝ	ㅝ	ㅝ	ㅝ	ㅝ	ㅝ

Let's combine ㅟ with the consonants we learned in the previous units. Remember to put the initial consonants on the upper-left, as ㅝ is a combination of a horizontal vowel ㅜ and a vertical vowel ㅓ.

궈	궈				
눠	눠				
둬	둬				
뤄	뤄				
뭐	뭐				
붜	붜				
쉬	쉬				
워	워				
줘	줘				
훠	훠				

쿼	쿼				
퉈	퉈				
풔	풔				
춰	춰				
꿔	꿔				
뚸	뚸				
뿨	뿨				
쒀	쒀				
쭤	쭤				

Part 2

Practice 1

 Listen carefully and choose one that includes the pronunciation of the letter marked on the left.

1. ㅐ ① ②

2. ㅔ ① ②

3. ㅒ ① ②

4. ㅖ ① ②

5. ㅘ ① ②

6. ㅝ ① ②

7. 게 ① ② ③

8. 화 ① ② ③

9. 쟤 ① ② ③

10. 눠 ① ② ③

11. 배 ① ② ③

12. 과 ① ② ③

13. 예 ① ② ③

14. 뭐 ① ② ③

15. 대 ① ② ③

Practice 2

 Listen carefully to the recordings and choose the letter that is pronounced.

1. 내 / 냬

2. 게 / 계

3. 매 / 먜

4. 솨 / 숴

5. 궈 / 과

6. 얘 / 애

7. 줘 / 좌

8. 례 / 래

9. 봐 / 붜

10. 케 / 켸

11. 와 / 애 / 예 / 워

12. 줘 / 제 / 재 / 좌

13. 개 / 궈 / 과 / 걔

14. 데 / 뎨 / 돠 / 둬

15. 뭐 / 매 / 메 / 몌

16. 화 / 훠 / 혜 / 해

17. 례 / 롸 / 뤄 / 레

18. 봐 / 배 / 뱨 / 붜

19. 얘 / 에 / 와 / 워

20. 세 / 솨 / 숴 / 셰

Practice 3

Write down and read the words below.

Shoulder

Curry

어eo	kk깨ae
어	깨

k카a	r레e
카	레

Story

Beautiful

애_{yae}	^g기_i
애	기

예_{ye}	^{pp}쁘_Ø	^d다_a
예	쁘	다

Apple

Cold

^s사_a	^g과_{wa}
사	과

^{ch}추_u	워_{wo}	요_{yo}
추	워	요

Fun

Crab

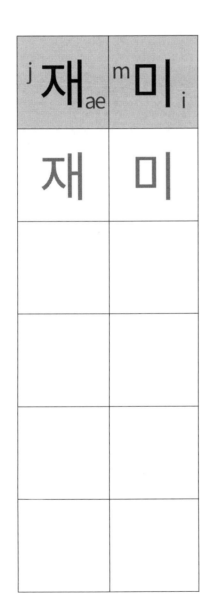

ʲ재ae	ᵐ미ᵢ
재	미

ᵍ게e
게

That Person   **Machine**

ʲ**재** yae
재

ᵍ**기**ᵢ	ᵍ**계**ye
기	계

Textbook

Hot

ᵍ교yo	ᵍ과wa	ˢ서eo
교	과	서

ᵈ더eo	워wo	요yo
더	워	요

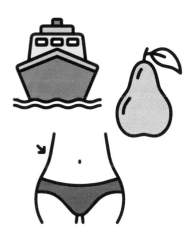

Ship / Pear / Belly

Korean Traditional Calligraphy

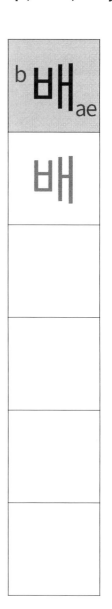

b배ae
배

s서eo	예ye
서	예

Face Washing

Confectionery

ˢ세ₑ	ˢ수ᵤ
세	수

ᵍ과_wa	ʲ자_a
과	자

Practice 4

Read the words below out loud, paying attention to the compound vowels.

1. 이 시계가 어디 거예요?

2. 저거 소화기예요.

3. 그녀 보러 타워에 가요.

4. 얘네 뭐 해요?

5. 무지개가 보여요.

6. 나무에서 매미가 노래해요.

7. 우리 어머니 피부가 고와요.

8. 아기가 저기 봐요.

9. 이거 고마워요.

10. 얘기가 아주 우스워요.

11. 거기에 나 데리고 가요.

12. 비가 와서 시끄러워요.

13. 우리 이제 헤어져요.

14. 대나무에서 소리가 나요.

15. 쓰레기 버리지 마세요.

16. 이제 자기 소개해요.

17. 자세가 나빠요.

18. 아저씨가 폐지 모아요.

19. 아버지께서 가계부 쓰세요.

20. 머리가 예뻐요.

Part 3

Practice 1

 Mark the wrong letter with an X and re-write the entire word after listening to the recordings. Each one will be read once. (Feel free to play more if you need.)

1. 교궈서 (textbook) → _____.

2. 어깨 (shoulder) → _____.

3. 셰수 (face washing) → _____.

4. 카례 (curry) → _____.

5. 추와요 (cold) → _____.

6. 사궈 (apple) → _____.

7. 서애 (Korean traditional calligraphy) → _____.

8. 궈자 (confectionery) → _____.

9. 졔 (that person) → _____.

10. 졔미 (fun) → _____.

11. 애쁘다 (beautiful) → _____.

12. 계 (crab) → _____.

13. 애기 (story) → _____.

14. 기게 (machine) → _____.

15. 더와요 (hot) → _____.

Practice 2

Listen carefully to the recordings and write down what you hear. Each one will be read once. (Feel free to play more if you need.)

1. _____.

2. _____.

3. _____.

4. _____.

5. _____.

6. _____.

7. _____.

8. _____.

9. _____.

10. _____.

11. _____.

12. _____.

13. _____.

14. _____.

15. _____.

16. _____.

17. _____.

18. _____.

19. _____.

20. _____.

제 8 과

모음 IV - Vowels IV

(ㅐ, ㅖ, ㅚ, ㅟ, ㅢ)

학습목표 OBJECTIVES

✓ How to read and write five compound vowels

✓ How to recognize five compound vowels in listening and in reading

✓ Learn some words that use different kinds of vowels and five compound vowels

Part 1

 Below are the five compound vowels in Korean. Listen carefully to the recordings and follow them. Each vowel will be read once. (Feel free to play more if you need.)

Sound Value: [we]

Way, Wag, Wagon

Current speakers of Standard Korean do not differentiate among the vowels ㅙ, ㅞ, and ㅚ in pronunciation.

Sound Value: [we]

Way, Wag, Wagon

Current speakers of Standard Korean do not differentiate among the vowels ㅙ, ㅞ, and ㅚ in pronunciation.

Sound Value: [we]

Way, Wag, Wagon

Current speakers of Standard Korean do not differentiate among the vowels ㅙ, ㅞ, and ㅚ in pronunciation.

Sound Value: [wi]

Window, Swiss, Wink

Sound Value: [ui]

None

There is no equivalent pronunciation of ㅢ in English. You can start pronouncing ㅡ first, and then slide to pronouncing ㅣ. ㅡ should be shorter than ㅣ.

Let's write each of them, paying attention to the stroke order.

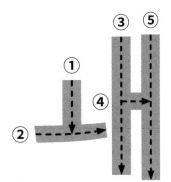

Sound Value: [we]

Way, Wag, Wagon

Current speakers of Standard Korean do not differentiate among the vowels ㅙ, ㅞ, and ㅚ in pronunciation.

ㅙ	ㅙ	ㅙ	ㅙ	ㅙ	ㅙ	ㅙ

Let's combine ㅙ with the consonants we learned in the previous units. Remember to put the initial consonants on the upper-left, as ㅙ is a combination of a horizontal vowel ㅗ and a vertical vowel ㅐ.

괘	괘				
놰	놰				
돼	돼				
뢔	뢔				
뫠	뫠				
봬	봬				
쇄	쇄				
왜	왜				
좨	좨				
홰	홰				

쾌	쾌				
퇘	퇘				
퐤	퐤				
쵀	쵀				
꽤	꽤				
뙈	뙈				
빼	빼				
쐐	쐐				
쫴	쫴				

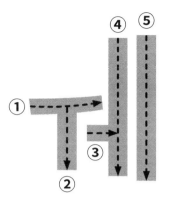

Sound Value: [we]

Way, Wag, Wagon

Current speakers of Standard Korean do not differentiate among the vowels ㅙ, ㅞ, and ㅚ in pronunciation.

ㅞ	ㅞ	ㅞ	ㅞ	ㅞ	ㅞ	ㅞ

Let's combine ㅞ with the consonants we learned in the previous units. Remember to put the initial consonants on the upper-left, as ㅞ is a combination of a horizontal vowel ㅜ and a vertical vowel ㅔ.

궤	궤				
눼	눼				
뒈	뒈				
뤠	뤠				
뭬	뭬				
뷔	뷔				
쉐	쉐				
웨	웨				
줴	줴				
훼	훼				

퀘	퀘				
퉤	퉤				
풰	풰				
췌	췌				
꿰	꿰				
뛔	뛔				
쀄	쀄				
쒜	쒜				
쮀	쮀				

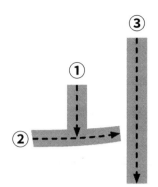

Sound Value: [we]

Way, Wag, Wagon

Current speakers of Standard Korean do not differentiate among the vowels ㅙ, ㅞ, and ㅚ in pronunciation.

ㅚ	ㅚ	ㅚ	ㅚ	ㅚ	ㅚ	ㅚ

Pronunciation Tip: be careful that the pronunciation of ㅚ does not correspond to ㅗ combined with ㅣ. The ending is closer to [e] sound.

Let's combine ㅚ with the consonants we learned in the previous units. Remember to put the initial consonants on the upper-left, as ㅚ is a combination of a horizontal vowel ㅗ and a vertical vowel ㅣ.

괴	괴				
뇌	뇌				
되	되				
뢰	뢰				
뫼	뫼				
뵈	뵈				
쇠	쇠				
외	외				
죄	죄				
회	회				

쾨	쾨				
퇴	퇴				
푀	푀				
최	최				
꾀	꾀				
뙤	뙤				
뾔	뾔				
쐬	쐬				
쬐	쬐				

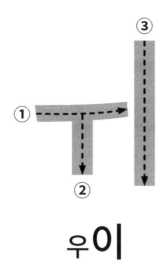

Sound Value: [wi]
Window, Swiss, Wink

To pronounce ㅟ correctly, you can start pronouncing ㅜ first, and then slide to pronouncing ㅣ. ㅜ should be shorter than ㅣ.

우이

ㅟ	ㅟ	ㅟ	ㅟ	ㅟ	ㅟ	ㅟ

Let's combine ㅟ with the consonants we learned in the previous units. Remember to put the initial consonants on the upper-left, as ㅟ is a combination of a horizontal vowel ㅜ and a vertical vowel ㅣ.

귀	귀				
뉘	뉘				
뒤	뒤				
뤼	뤼				
뮈	뮈				
뷔	뷔				
쉬	쉬				
위	위				
쥐	쥐				
휘	휘				

퀴	퀴				
튀	튀				
퓌	퓌				
취	취				
뀌	뀌				
뛰	뛰				
쀠	쀠				
쒸	쒸				
쮜	쮜				

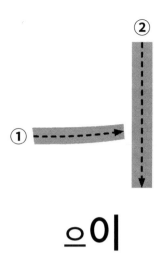

Sound Value: [ui]

Wow, What, Watch

There is no equivalent pronunciation of ⊣ in English. You can start pronouncing — first, and then slide to pronouncing │ . — should be shorter than │ .

의

⊣	⊣	⊣	⊣	⊣	⊣	⊣

Let's combine ⊣ with the consonants we learned in the previous units. Remember to put the initial consonants on the upper-left, as ⊣ is a combination of a horizontal vowel — and a vertical vowel ㅣ.

긔	긔				
늬	늬				
듸	듸				
릐	릐				
믜	믜				
븨	븨				
싀	싀				
의	의				
즤	즤				
희	희				

키	키				
티	티				
피	피				
치	치				
끼	끼				
띠	띠				
삐	삐				
씨	씨				
찌	찌				

Part 2

Practice 1

 Listen carefully and choose one that includes the pronunciation of the letter marked on the left.

1. ㅙ ① ②

2. ㅖ ① ②

3. ㅚ ① ②

4. ㅝ ① ②

5. ㅢ ① ②

6. ㅝ ① ②

7. 돼 ① ② ③

8. 휘 ① ② ③

9. 의 ① ② ③

10. 눼 ① ② ③

11. 귀 ① ② ③

12. 죄 ① ② ③

13. 외 ① ② ③

14. 뒤 ① ② ③

15. 믜 ① ② ③

Practice 2

 Listen carefully to the recordings and choose the letter that is pronounced.

1. 괴 / 긔

2. 놰 / 뉘

3. 휘 / 희

4. 쉐 / 쉬

5. 의 / 왜

6. 뤠 / 뤼

7. 즤 / 죄

8. 례 / 뤼 / 뤠

9. 븨 / 봬 / 붜

10. 뮈 / 믜 / 매

11. 과 / 괘 / 귀

12. 둬 / 뒤 / 되

13. 해 / 회 / 휘

14. 쥐 / 쟤 / 죄

15. 훠 / 혜 / 해 / 훼

16. 걔 / 개 / 괴 / 궈

17. 솨 / 쉬 / 쇄 / 숴

18. 뷔 / 봬 / 붸 / 붜

19. 채 / 취 / 춰 / 최

20. 퇴 / 퉤 / 튀 / 퉈

Practice 3

Write down and read the words below.

Brain

Wheel

^d두_u	ⁿ뇌_{we}		^b바_a	^k퀴_{wi}
두	뇌		바	퀴

Pig

Chair

ᵈ돼ᵥₑ	ʲ지ᵢ
돼	지

의ᵤᵢ	ʲ자ₐ
의	자

Sweater

Lonely

[s]스[ø]	웨[we]	[t]터[eo]
스	웨	터

외[we]	[r]로[o]	워[wo]
외	로	워

Doctor

Quiz

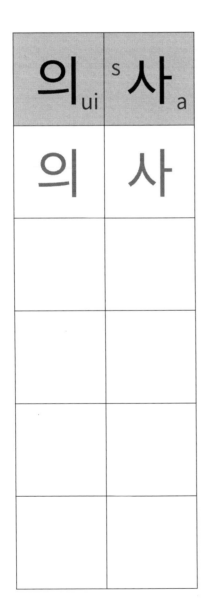

의 ᵘⁱ	ˢ 사 ₐ
의	사

ᵏ 퀴 wi	ʲ 즈 ø
퀴	즈

Why

Destruction

왜 we
왜

p파 a	g괴 we
파	괴

Ear

Waiter

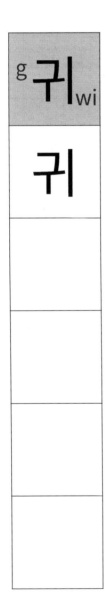

g귀wi
귀

웨we	이i	t터eo
웨	이	터

Pattern, Design

Shake

^m 무 _u	^n 늬 _ui
무	늬

^s 쉐 _we	이 _i	^k 크 _ø
쉐	이	크

Practice 4

Read the words below out loud, paying attention to the compound vowels.

1. 토끼가 빠르게 뛰어가요.

2. 왜 머리가 아파요?

3. 빼기가 더 어려워요.

4. 지구의 궤도

5. 외가의 아저씨가 오시네요.

6. 위에 허수아비가 보여요.

7. 스웨터가 너무 더워요.

8. 꼬마야 이리 와서 보아라.

9. 아기 돼지의 꼬리가 귀여워요.

10. 꾀꼬리 따라 노래해요.

11. 빠르게 뛰어서 더워요.

12. 아빠하고 오빠하고 사과 쉐이크 마셔요.

13. 이 드라마 무서워요.

14. 모두 사라져서 외로워요.

15. 이거 요리해줘요.

16. 뒤에서 새끼 돼지가 따라와요.

Part 3

Practice 1

 Mark the wrong letter with an X and re-write the entire word after listening to the recordings. Each one will be read once. (Feel free to play more if you need.)

1. 궤 (ear) → _____.

2. 되지 (pig) → _____.

3. 두놰 (brain) → _____.

4. 무늬 (pattern, design) → _____.

5. 바킈 (wheel) → _____.

6. 쇄이크 (shake) → _____.

7. 스위터 (sweater) → _____.

8. 웨 (why) → _____.

9. 의로워 (lonely) → _____.

10. 위이터 (waiter) → _____.

11. 외사 (doctor) → _____.

12. 웨자 (chair) → _____.

13. 킈즈 (quiz) → _____.

14. 파괘 (destruction) → _____.

Practice 2

 Listen carefully to the recordings and write down what you hear. Each one will be read once. (Feel free to play more if you need.)

1. _____ .

2. _____ .

3. _____ .

4. _____ .

5. _____ .

6. _____ .

7. _____ .

8. _____ .

9. _____ .

10. _____ .

11. _____ .

12. _____ .

13. _____ .

14. _____ .

15. _____ .

16. _____ .

17. _____ .

18. _____ .

19. _____ .

20. _____ .

제9과

받침 – Final Consonants

학습목표 OBJECTIVES

✓ How to write and read final consonants

✓ How to recognize final consonants in listening

✓ Learn some words with different kinds of final consonants

Part 1

Final consonants in the Korean language can be classified into 8 categories according to how they are pronounced. When a consonant is at a final position, you may not hear the entire pronunciation of the original character. Final consonants are generally shorter and the articulation stops before the releasing stage.

The table below shows the classification.

Final Consonants	Pronunciation
ㄴ	ㄴ [n]
ㄹ	ㄹ [l]
ㅁ	ㅁ [m]
ㅇ	ㅇ [ŋ]
ㅂ, ㅍ	ㅂ [p]
ㄱ, ㄲ, ㅋ	ㄱ [k]
ㄷ, ㅅ, ㅆ, ㅈ, ㅊ, ㅌ, ㅎ	ㄷ [t]
Double Final Consonants	Irregular

Before we learn about each kind of final consonants, let us take an overall look at the structure of syllabic blocks. As you have already studied, each Hangul character is a syllabic block made up of both consonants and vowels. Syllables are mostly made up according to the CVC (consonant + vowel + consonant) structure, and when there is no initial consonant, we use 'ㅇ' as a filler, whereas we leave the third place empty when there is no final consonant. There are two different locations for vowels; one is vertical for ㅏ, ㅑ, ㅓ, ㅕ, ㅣ and the other is horizontal for ㅗ, ㅛ, ㅜ, ㅠ, ㅡ. The ordering of consonants and vowels is indicated below.

C	V	나, 비	C / V	노, 루	C / V	와, 쥐
C	V					
C	V / C	정, 말	C / V / C	문, 틀	C / V / C	원, 활

Now let's practice how to write and read final consonants of each category. You can also pay attention to broadening your vocabulary in this part.

Final Consonants	Pronunciation
ㄴ	ㄴ [n]

 Listen carefully to the recordings and read the words below following the recordings. Each one will be read once. After that, write the words filling in the empty boxes.

산 mountain	산				
손 hand	손				

눈						
eye / snow	눈					

인사				
greeting	인사			

친구				
friend	친구			

우산				
umbrella	우산			

언니				
older sister	언니			

자전거			
bicycle	자전거		

전화기			
telephone	전화기		

휴대폰			
cellphone	휴대폰		

Final Consonants	Pronunciation
ㄹ	ㄹ [l]

Listen carefully to the recordings and read the words below following the recordings. Each one will be read once. After that, write the words filling in the empty boxes.

물 water	물					

별 star	별					

달 Moon, month	달					

가을 fall, autumn	가을			

겨울 winter	겨울			

신발 shoe	신발			

얼굴 face	얼굴			

할머니 grandmother	할머니		

지하철 subway	지하철		

일요일 Sunday	일요일		

Final Consonants	Pronunciation
ㅁ	ㅁ [m]

Listen carefully to the recordings and read the words below following the recordings. Each one will be read once. After that, write the words filling in the empty boxes.

봄 spring	봄				

밤 night / chestnut	밤				

힘	힘					
power						

여름	여름			
summer				

엄마	엄마			
mom				

구름	구름			
cloud				

바람	바람			
wind				

컴퓨터	컴퓨터		
computer			

편의점	편의점		
convenience store			

금요일	금요일		
Friday			

Final Consonants	Pronunciation
ㅇ	ㅇ [ŋ]

Listen carefully to the recordings and read the words below following the recordings. Each one will be read once. After that, write the words filling in the empty boxes.

공 (ball)	공					

병 (bottle / disease)	병					

빵 (bread)	빵					

태양 (Sun)	태양			

당근 (carrot)	당근			

동생 (younger sibling)	동생			

공부	공부			
study				

오징어	오징어		
squid			

강아지	강아지		
puppy			

고양이	고양이		
cat			

Final Consonants	Pronunciation
ㅂ, ㅍ	ㅂ [p]

Listen carefully to the recordings and read the words below following the recordings. Each one will be read once. After that, write the words filling in the empty boxes.

밥	밥				
meal / rice					

입	입				
mouth					

잎						
leaf	잎					

지갑				
wallet	지갑			

무릎				
knee	무릎			

수업				
lesson	수업			

장갑				
glove	장갑			

비빔밥			
Bibimbap	비빔밥		

앞치마			
apron	앞치마		

립스틱			
lipstick	립스틱		

Final Consonants	Pronunciation
ㄱ,ㄲ,ㅋ	ㄱ [k]

Listen carefully to the recordings and read the words below following the recordings. Each one will be read once. After that, write the words filling in the empty boxes.

약 medication	약				

밖 outside	밖				

턱 jaw / chin	턱				

수박 watermelon	수박		

부엌 kitchen	부엌		

낚시 fishing	낚시		

저녁	저녁			
evening				

옥수수	옥수수		
corn			

목소리	목소리		
voice			

세탁기	세탁기		
washing machine			

Final Consonants	Pronunciation
ㄷ, ㅅ, ㅆ, ㅈ, ㅊ, ㅌ, ㅎ	ㄷ [t]

🎧 Listen carefully to the recordings and read the words below following the recordings. Each one will be read once. After that, write the words filling in the empty boxes.

꽃	꽃				
flower					

밑	밑				
bottom					

맛	맛					
flavor						

로봇	로봇			
robot				

낮잠	낮잠			
nap				

버섯	버섯			
mushroom				

있다	있다			
to exist / to have				

젓가락	젓가락		
chopsticks			

가마솥	가마솥		
iron pot			

돋보기	돋보기		
magnifying glass			

Final Consonants	Pronunciation
Double Final Consonants	Irregular

There are 11 pairs of double consonants that can be found at the final position (Double consonants are never used as a primary consonant). In most pairs, only the first sound is pronounced and the second character is omitted. However, for ㄺ, ㄻ and ㄿ, only the second sound should be pronounced.

 Listen carefully to the recordings and read the words below following the recordings. Each one will be read once. After that, write the words filling in the empty boxes.

Exceptions:

1) 밟- [밥] when followed by a consonant

2) 넓- [넙] in certain words such as 넓죽하다 or 넓둥글다

3) ㄺ is pronounced as [ㄹ] when it is followed by ㄱ

값 갑 price	값				

몫 목 share	몫				

여덟 여덜 eight	여덟			

없다	없다			
업따				
to not exist / to not have				

앉다	앉다			
안따				
to sit				

닭	닭				
닥					
chicken					

삶	삶				
삼					
life					

늙다	늙다			
늑따				
to be old / to age				

젊다	젊다			
점따				
to be young				

읽다	읽다			
익따				
to read				

Part 2

Practice 1

 Listen carefully and choose one that includes the pronunciation of the letter marked on the left.

1. ㄹ ① ② ③

2. ㅇ ① ② ③

3. ㅂ ① ② ③

4. ㄱ ① ② ③

5. ㅅ ① ② ③

6. ㄴ ① ② ③

7. ㅍ ① ② ③

8. ㅋ ① ② ③

9. ㅊ ① ② ③

10. ㅌ ① ② ③

11. ㄲ ① ② ③

12. ㅃ ① ② ③

13. ㄹ ① ② ③

14. ㅈ ① ② ③

15. ㄴ ① ② ③

Practice 2

 Listen carefully to the recordings and choose the letter that is pronounced.

1. 동 / 돌 / 돗

2. 꼭 / 꽁 / 꼼

3. 법 / 범 / 벗

4. 밭 / 반 / 밤

5. 앙 / 앞 / 안

6. 입 / 일 / 익

7. 값 / 간 / 갓

8. 념 / 녁 / 녕

9. 산 / 삶 / 삽

10. 맵 / 맨 / 맥

11. 탑 / 탓 / 탐

12. 싼 / 쌀 / 쌈

13. 춤 / 춥 / 춘

14. 덛 / 덮 / 덜

15. 콩 / 콜 / 콧

16. 억 / 엇 / 얼

17. 편 / 폄 / 폭

18. 닻 / 닭 / 답

19. 쨍 / 쨈 / 쨀

20. 깔 / 깝 / 깡

Practice 3

 Listen carefully and choose one that includes the pronunciation of the letter marked on the left.

1. ① ㄴ   ② ㄹ   ③ ㅅ   ④ ㅂ

2. ① ㅇ   ② ㅎ   ③ ㄴ   ④ ㄱ

3. ① ㅌ   ② ㄴ   ③ ㄹ   ④ ㅍ

4. ① ㅇ   ② ㅆ   ③ ㅁ   ④ ㄴ

5. ① ㄴ   ② ㅂ   ③ ㄲ   ④ ㄹ

6. ① ㅋ   ② ㄷ   ③ ㄴ   ④ ㅇ

7. ① ㄹ   ② ㄴ   ③ ㅁ   ④ ㅍ

8. ① ㅇ   ② ㅈ   ③ ㄱ   ④ ㄴ

9. ① ㄴ   ② ㄹ   ③ ㅂ   ④ ㅇ

10. ① ㄲ   ② ㅊ   ③ ㄴ   ④ ㅁ

11. ① ㅍ   ② ㄴ   ③ ㄹ   ④ ㅇ

12. ① ㅁ   ② ㅌ   ③ ㅋ   ④ ㄴ

13. ① ㅂ   ② ㅇ   ③ ㄴ   ④ ㄹ

14. ① ㄴ   ② ㅎ   ③ ㅁ   ④ ㄱ

15. ① ㄹ   ② ㅇ   ③ ㅍ   ④ ㄴ

Practice 4

Listen carefully to the recordings and circle as many letters as possible that have the same pronunciation of the final consonants as what you hear.

1. 가을 하늘의 구름이 예뻐요.

2. 내 가방에는 립스틱이 있다.

3. 당근을 물에 담가요.

4. 금요일 저녁에는 지하철을 안 타요.

5. 세탁기 소리가 너무 커요.

6. 편의점에서 오징어를 팔아요.

7. 낚시하러 일요일에 가요.

8. 앞치마를 하고 비빔밥을 만들어요.

9. 식탁 위에 있는 꽃 너무 아름다워요.

10. 동생은 지금 공부를 해요.

11. 물을 마시고 나서 옥수수를 먹어요.

12. 낮잠을 자면 저녁에 잠이 안 와요.

13. 우리 집 강아지는 수박을 먹어요.

14. 여덟 명의 목소리가 들려요.

15. 겨울이 되면 무릎이 아파요.

Practice 5

Listen carefully to the recordings and fill in the blanks with appropriate final consonants as shown in the sample. Mark X in the box when there is no final consonant. Each one will be read once. (Feel free to play more if you need.)

Sample	
다	그
ㅇ	ㄴ

1.

커	퓨	터

4.

로	보

2.

태	야

5.

저	가	라

3.

어	구

6.

아	치	마

7.

8.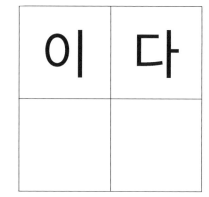

9.

10.

Practice 6

 Mark the wrong letter with an X and re-write the entire word after listening to the recordings. Each one will be read once. (Feel free to play more if you need.)

1. 버섬 _____.
2. 고얀이 _____.
3. 장값 _____.
4. 늘다 _____.
5. 세탉기 _____.
6. 가마솟 _____.
7. 낙시 _____.
8. 컨퓨터 _____.
9. 수엎 _____.
10. 꼿 _____.
11. 점다 _____.
12. 여릉 _____.
13. 엄굼 _____.
14. 옵수수 _____.
15. 맆스틱 _____.

16. 낱잠 _____.
17. 감아지 _____.
18. 곤부 _____.
19. 절가락 _____.
20. 근요일 _____.
21. 로봅 _____.
22. 잔갑 _____.
23. 빨 _____.
24. 몹소리 _____.
25. 돈생 _____.
26. 악치마 _____.
27. 밧 _____.
28. 돕보기 _____.
29. 담근 _____.
30. 가응 _____.

Practice 7

 Listen carefully to the recordings and fill in the blanks with an appropriate letter. Each one will be read once. (Feel free to play more if you need.)

1. ☐ 머니
2. ☐ 마
3. ☐ 아지
4. 수 ☐
5. 저 ☐
6. 버 ☐
7. ☐ 다
8. ☐ 화기
9. 신 ☐
10. 바 ☐
11. ☐
12. 무 ☐
13. 부 ☐
14. ☐
15. 여 ☐

16. 휴대 ☐
17. ☐ 구
18. ☐
19. ☐
20. ☐ 부
21. ☐
22. 수 ☐
23. ☐ 보기
24. ☐ 다
25. ☐ 니
26. 우 ☐
27. 겨 ☐
28. ☐
29. 지 ☐
30. ☐

Practice 8

Choose the word that is pronounced as presented.

1. 박 　　　 ① 밖 　　　 ② 밤 　　　 ③ 밭

2. 삼 　　　 ① 살 　　　 ② 삶 　　　 ③ 삵

3. 안따 　　 ① 알다 　　 ② 앓다 　　 ③ 앉다

4. 믿 　　　 ① 믹 　　　 ② 밑 　　　 ③ 밍

5. 입 　　　 ① 잎 　　　 ② 읽 　　　 ③ 일

6. 업따 　　 ① 엄다 　　 ② 없다 　　 ③ 얼다

7. 약 　　　 ① 얌 　　　 ② 양 　　　 ③ 약

8. 여덜 　　 ① 여덟 　　 ② 여던 　　 ③ 여덤

9. 로볻 　　 ① 로볶 　　 ② 로봇 　　 ③ 로본

10. 버섣 　　 ① 버석 　　 ② 버섰 　　 ③ 버섯

11. 무릅 　　 ① 무릎 　　 ② 무릇 　　 ③ 무릍

12. 늑따 　　 ① 늡다 　　 ② 늛다 　　 ③ 늙다

13. 갑 　　　 ① 값 　　　 ② 갇 　　　 ③ 갓

14. 압치마 　 ① 암치마 　 ② 앞치마 　 ③ 악치마

15. 부억 　　 ① 부엍 　　 ② 부엉 　　 ③ 부엌

Practice 9

 Listen carefully to the recordings and choose the right pronunciation of the given words. Each one will be read once. (Feel free to play more if you need.)

1. 옛 (old)   ①   ②

2. 첫 (first)   ①   ②

3. 낱 (each)   ①   ②

4. 빚 (debt)   ①   ②

5. 숲 (forest)   ①   ②

6. 찢다 (to tear)   ①   ②

7. 빛 (light)   ①   ②

8. 침대 (bed)   ①   ②

9. 놓치다 (to miss out on)   ①   ②

10. 호박 (pumpkin)   ①   ②

11. 날개 (wing)   ①   ②

12. 컵 (cup)   ①   ②

13. 곧 (soon)   ①   ②

14. 옷 (clothes)   ①   ②

15. 섞다 (to mix)   ①   ②

Practice 10

Below are the commonly used English words in the Korean language. Choose the right transcription of the given words.

1. Lipstick   ① 립스틱   ② 립스팃   ③ 림스틱

2. Computer   ① 컴퓨터   ② 컨퓨터   ③ 컹퓨터

3. Hotdog   ① 합도그   ② 할도그   ③ 핫도그

4. Digital   ① 디지턴   ② 디지텁   ③ 디지털

5. Cream   ① 크링   ② 크림   ③ 크린

6. Necktie   ① 넥타이   ② 넬타이   ③ 넴타이

7. Concert   ① 콘서트   ② 콩서트   ③ 콤서트

8. E-mail   ① 이메인   ② 이메임   ③ 이메일

9. Game   ① 게임   ② 게인   ③ 게잇

10. Taxi   ① 탠시   ② 택시   ③ 탭시

11. Olive   ① 옹리브   ② 올리브   ③ 온리브

12. Internet   ① 인터넥   ② 인터넵   ③ 인터넷

13. Coffee shop   ① 커피숍   ② 커피숌   ③ 커피솔

14. Model   ① 모뎀   ② 모덴   ③ 모델

15. Tip   ① 팁   ② 팁   ③ 틱

Part 3

Practice 1

Below are some of the phrases you can easily find on the signages in Korea. Read them out loud, paying attention to the final consonants.

1. 계단에서 뛰지 마세요. (Do not run on the stairs)

2. 공사중 (Under construction)

3. 금연구역입니다. (This is a non-smoking area)

4. 화장실 (Restroom)

5. 일방통행 (One-way road)

6. 고정문 (Fixed door)

7. 당기세요 (Pull the door)

8. 주차장 (Parking area)

9. 출입구 (Entrance)

10. 휴대폰 사용금지 (Mobile phones are not allowed)

11. 냉방중 (Air-conditioning)

12. 탑승금지 (Do not board)

13. 미끄럼주의 (Wet floor)

14. 청소중 (Cleaning is in progress)

15. 머리조심 (Watch your head)

Practice 2

Below are some of the names of the cities and islands in Korea marked on the map. Read them out loud, paying attention to the final consonants.

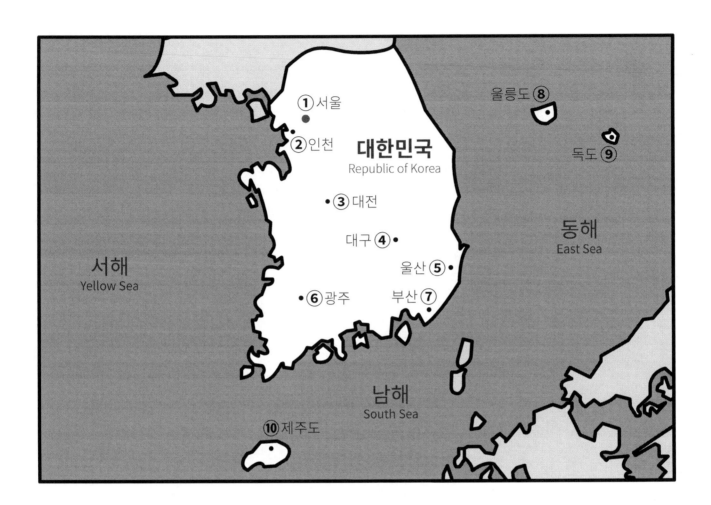

1. 서울

2. 인천

3. 대전

4. 대구

5. 울산

6. 광주

7. 부산

8. 울릉도

9. 독도

10. 제주도

Practice 3

Transcribe the English names given below into Hangul as shown in the example.

> **Example**
>
> John → 존

1. **Christine**   →   _____.

2. **Michael**   →   _____.

3. **Nicky**   →   _____.

4. **Lisa**   →   _____.

5. **Patrick**   →   _____.

6. **Olivia**   →   _____.

7. **Paul**   →   _____.

8. **Stephanie**   →   _____.

9. **Jimmy**   →   _____.

10. **Tim**   →   _____.

Practice 4

Now you can hear some of the common words that Korean people use in their everyday situations. Listen carefully to the recordings and fill in the blanks with an appropriate letter. Each one will be read once. (Feel free to play more if you need.)

1. ☐ 식 (snack)

2. 거 ☐ (living room)

3. 기 ☐ (joy)

4. ☐ 밥 (gimbap)

5. 남 ☐ (husband)

6. ☐ 물 (animal)

7. 레스토 ☐ (restaurant)

8. 메뉴 ☐ (menu)

9. 백화 ☐ (department store)

10. 사 ☐ (love)

11. ☐ 거지 (dish-washing)

12. 쇼핑 ☐ (shopping mall)

13. 스 ☐ (skin)

14. ☐ 기 (musical instrument)

15. ☐ 양제 (nutritional supplements)

16. ☐ 화 (movie)

17. 옆 ☐ (next door)

18. 음 ☐ (music)

19. ☐ 속 (connection)

20. 주 ☐ (ordering)

21. 주 ☐ (owner)

22. 친 ☐ (kindness)

23. ☐ 배 (package)

24. 테이 ☐ (table)

25. 텔레비 ☐ (television)

26. 포 ☐ 지 (wrapping paper)

27. 행 ☐ (happiness)

28. 화 ☐ (flower pot)

29. 화장 ☐ (cosmetics)

30. 희 ☐ (hope)

Practice 5

 Listen carefully to the recordings and write down what you hear. Each one will be read once. (Feel free to play more if you need.)

1. _____.

2. _____.

3. _____.

4. _____.

5. _____.

6. _____.

7. _____.

8. _____.

9. _____.

10. _____.

11. _____.

12. _____.

13. _____.

14. _____.

15. _____.

16. _____.

17. _____.

18. _____.

19. _____.

20. _____.

CHECK UP
(UNIT 1 – UNIT 9)

Practice 1

 Listen carefully to the recordings and circle the words you can hear and write them down below as shown in the example. Each one will be read once. (Feel free to play more if you need.)

커	피	강	아	지	과	웨
편	자	태	저	빠	자	이
의	사	양	씨	스	웨	터
점	더	금	교	과	서	예
추	워	요	세	탁	기	장
일	요	일	수	보	갑	인
젊	다	채	돋	길	밥	혼

Example

장갑

1. _____.

2. _____.

3. _____.

4. _____.

5. _____.

6. _____.

7. _____.

8. _____.

9. _____.

10. _____.

11. _____.

12. _____.

13. _____.

14. _____.

15. _____.

Practice 2

Below are the names of some cities in the US and their Korean transcription. Read them out loud and draw a matching line as shown in the example.

Example 뉴욕 •	• Las Vegas
1. 워싱턴 •	• Atlanta
2. 로스앤젤레스 •	• Boston
3. 시애틀 •	• Miami
4. 애틀랜타 •	• New York
5. 샌프란시스코 •	• Philadelphia
6. 필라델피아 •	• Detroit
7. 휴스턴 •	• Washington
8. 시카고 •	• Denver
9. 보스턴 •	• San Francisco
10. 마이애미 •	• San Diego
11. 샌디에이고 •	• Los Angeles
12. 댈러스 •	• Dallas
13. 디트로이트 •	• Seattle
14. 덴버 •	• Houston
15. 라스베가스 •	• Chicago

Practice 3

 Listen carefully to the recordings and write down what you hear. Each one will be read once.
(Feel free to play more if you need.)

1. _____.

2. _____.

3. _____.

4. _____.

5. _____.

6. _____.

7. _____.

8. _____.

9. _____.

10. _____.

11. _____.

12. _____.

13. _____.

14. _____.

15. _____.

16. _____.

17. _____.

18. _____.

19. _____.

20. _____.

NOTES

제 2 장

발음 규칙

CHAPTER 2
PRONUNCIATION RULES

제10과

발음규칙 I
Liaison

학습목표 OBJECTIVES

- ✓ How to read final consonants, ㄱ, ㄴ, ㄹ, ㅁ, ㅂ when placed before a letter of no initial consonant
- ✓ How to read final consonants, ㅋ, ㄲ, ㅍ, ㄷ, ㅅ, ㅆ, ㅈ, ㅊ, ㅌ when placed before a letter of no initial consonant
- ✓ How to read double final consonants when placed before a letter of no initial consonant

Part 1

First, let's learn how to read final consonants, ㄱ, ㄴ, ㄹ, ㅁ, ㅂ when they are placed before a letter of no initial consonant.

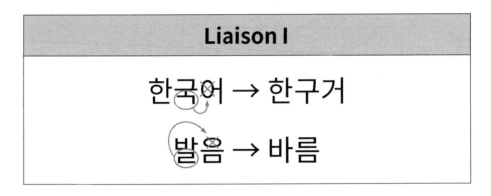

Liaison I
한국어 → 한구거
발음 → 바름

When a syllable begins with a vowel sound, then the consonant 'ㅇ' will act as a silent placeholder. Therefore, when a letter with a final consonant is followed by a letter starting with a placeholder 'ㅇ,' it takes the place of 'ㅇ,' and combines with the vowel that is written with 'ㅇ.'

Here are some of the examples of Liaison I.

낙엽 (fallen leaves)	→	나겹
미국인 (American)	→	미구긴
어린이 (child)	→	어리니
안전운전 (safe driving)	→	안저눈전
할아버지 (grandpa)	→	하라버지
얼음 (ice)	→	어름
금요일 (Friday)	→	그묘일
다듬어 (다듬다: to trim)	→	다드머
접이식 (foldable)	→	저비식
밥을 (밥: rice)	→	바블

Now please write down the pronunciation of the given words.

1. 거북이 (turtle)

_____.

2. 사람을 (사람: person)

_____.

3. 졸업은 (졸업: graduation)

_____.

4. 귀걸이 (earring)

_____.

5. 대문으로 (대문: gate)

_____.

Second, let's learn how to read final consonants, ㅋ, ㄲ, ㅍ, ㄷ, ㅅ, ㅆ, ㅈ, ㅊ, ㅌ when they are placed before a letter of no initial consonant.

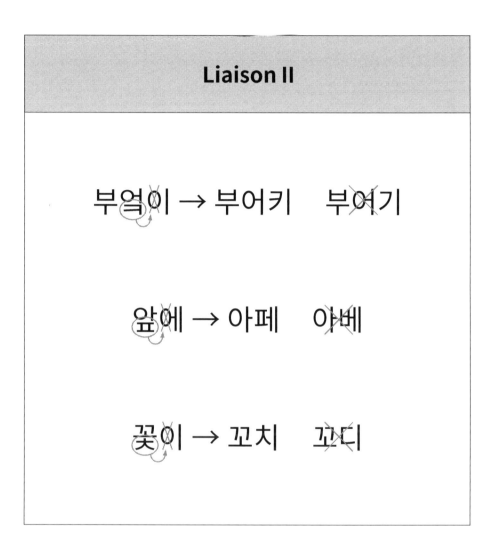

Previously, you have learned that the final consonants ㅋ, ㄲ are pronounced as [ㄱ], ㅍ is pronounced as [ㅂ], and ㄷ, ㅅ, ㅆ, ㅈ, ㅊ, ㅌ are all pronounced as [ㄷ].

However, when those final consonants are followed by a syllable with no initial consonant, this rule is ignored. You can just combine the final consonant with the vowel of the following letter and pronounce as they are.

Be careful that the final consonant ㅎ does not follow this rule. So, 좋아 should be read as [조아]. The final ㅎ does not have any sound, when it is placed before a letter with no initial consonant.

Here are some of the examples of Liaison II.

낮에 (낮: daytime)	→	나제
눈높이 (eye level)	→	눈노피
맛이 (맛: flavor)	→	마시
무릎이 (무릎: knee)	→	무르피
받아 (받다: to receive)	→	바다
밭에 (밭: farm)	→	바테
빛이 (빛: light)	→	비치
섞어 (섞다: to mix)	→	서꺼
씻어 (씻다: to wash)	→	씨서
있어요 (있다: to exist)	→	이써요

Now please write down the pronunciation of the given words.

1. 찢어진 (torn)   → _____.

2. 닫으세요 (닫다: close)   → _____.

3. 볶음밥 (fried rice)   → _____.

4. 잎에 (잎: leaf)   → _____.

5. 쫓아가다 (to chase)   → _____.

Lastly, let's learn how to read double final consonants when they are placed before a letter of no initial consonant.

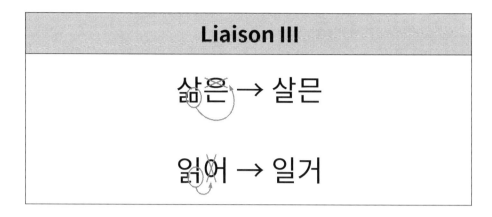

Liaison III

삶은 → 살믄

읽어 → 일거

When double final consonants are followed by a letter of no initial consonant, the first one of the double final consonants remains at its place, but the second one combines with the vowel of the following letter.

Here are some of the examples of Liaison III.

닭이 (닭: chicken)   →   달기

젊은 (young)   →   절믄

늙은 (old)   →   늘근

넓이 (area)   →   널비

밟아 (밟다: to step on)   →   발바

굶어 (굶다: to starve)   →   굴머

핥아 (핥다: to lick)   →   할타

읊어 (읊다: to recite)   →   을퍼

긁어 (긁다: to scratch)   →   글거

앉아 (앉다: to sit)   →   안자

Now please write down the pronunciation of the given words.

1. 닮아 (닮다: to resemble)

_____.

2. 맑아요 (맑다: clear)

_____.

3. 밝은 (bright)

_____.

4. 짧아 (짧다: short)

_____.

5. 옮아 (옮다: to be infected)

_____.

Part 2

Practice 1

Choose the right pronunciation of the words given below.

1. 같은 ① 가튼 ② 가든
2. 공원에 ① 공워네 ② 공워레
3. 깊이 ① 기비 ② 기피
4. 깎아 ① 까가 ② 까까
5. 나들이 ① 나드리 ② 나들리
6. 높여 ① 노벼 ② 노펴
7. 맑아 ① 말가 ② 마가
8. 믿음 ① 미듬 ② 미슴
9. 바깥으로 ① 바까드로 ② 바까트로
10. 밖에서 ① 바께서 ② 바게서
11. 버릇이 ① 버르시 ② 버르디
12. 앞으로 ① 아브로 ② 아프로
13. 옷을 ① 오들 ② 오슬
14. 찾아 ① 차자 ② 차다
15. 책을 ① 채글 ② 책글

Practice 2

 Listen carefully to the recordings and choose the right pronunciation of the given words. Each one will be read once.

1. 지킴이 ① ②
2. 먹이 ① ②
3. 녹여 ① ②
4. 있어라 ① ②
5. 손에 ① ②
6. 기억을 ① ②
7. 앙갚음 ① ②
8. 싶어 ① ②
9. 덮어주다 ① ②
10. 낚아 ① ②

11. 꿀맛이다 ① ②
12. 땀이 ① ②
13. 꽃에 ① ②
14. 뽑아야 ① ②
15. 맞은 ① ②
16. 무엇이 ① ②
17. 물건을 ① ②
18. 형님은 ① ②
19. 맡으며 ① ②
20. 거짓을 ① ②

Practice 3

 Listen carefully to the recordings and fill in the blanks by writing down an appropriate letter. Each word will be read once. (Feel free to play more if you need.)

1. ☐ 은

2. 마 ☐ 에

3. 여 ☐ 엔

4. ☐ 으로

5. 덮 ☐

6. ☐ 아라

7. 돈 ☐

8. ☐ 아서

9. ☐ 으면

10. 얼 ☐ 판

11. 부모님 ☐

12. 나 ☐ 이

13. 됨 ☐ 이

14. 음 ☐ 을

15. ☐ 어

16. ☐ 어요

17. ☐ 아

18. ☐ 을

19. 신 ☐ 을

20. 물어 ☐ 은

Part 3

Practice 1

Read carefully the sentences below and circle the letters that the Liaison rule can be applied. Each sentence has two answers.

1. 봄바람이 시원하게 불어오네요.

2. 여름은 아이스크림의 계절.

3. 가을에는 사랑하는 사람에게 편지를 써요.

4. 이번 겨울에는 등산을 할 거예요.

5. 우리 강아지는 낮에 잠을 자요.

6. 밥을 먹고 나서 산책을 해요.

7. 이불을 잘 덮으면 감기에 안 걸려요.

8. 날씨가 추워져서 두꺼운 옷을 입어야 해요.

9. 낮에 커피를 안 마셔서 잠이 와요.

10. 한국음식 먹으러 가요.

11. 뚜껑을 닫아야 안심이 돼요.

12. 큰 소리가 나서 밖을 보니 택배가 왔어요.

13. 엄마네 밭에는 수박이 잘 자라요.

14. 우리 형님은 사업을 크게 하세요.

15. 한국어를 배우려면 한국에 대해 공부해야 해요.

Practice 2

 Listen carefully to the recordings and write down what you hear. Each one will be read once. (Feel free to play more if you need.)

1. _____.

2. _____.

3. _____.

4. _____.

5. _____.

6. _____.

7. _____.

8. _____.

9. _____.

10. _____.

11. _____.

12. _____.

13. _____.

14. _____.

15. _____.

16. _____.

17. _____.

18. _____.

19. _____.

20. _____.

제11과

발음규칙 II
Tensification

학습목표 OBJECTIVES

✓ How to read words correctly when final consonants, [ㄱ], [ㄷ], [ㅂ] tensify an initial consonant of the following letter

✓ How to read words correctly when final consonants, [ㄴ], [ㄹ], [ㅁ], [ㅇ] tensify an initial consonant of the following letter

Part 1

First, let's learn how to pronounce when the final consonants, ㄱ, ㄷ, and ㅂ are placed before an initial consonant of the following letter.

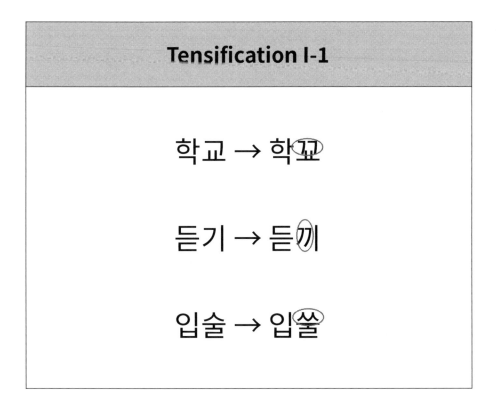

When the final consonants are ㄱ, ㄷ, or ㅂ, and are placed before the initial consonant of the following letter, they make the following initial consonant into a tense sound.

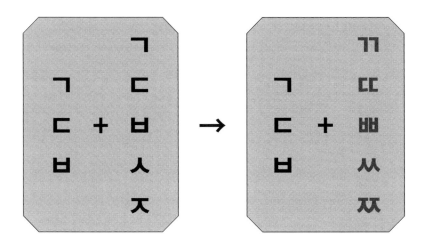

Here are some of the examples of Tensification I-1.

책장 (bookshelf)	→	책짱
걷기 (walking)	→	걷끼
밥상 (dining table)	→	밥쌍
국밥 (rice served in soup)	→	국빱
접시 (plate)	→	접씨
약속 (appointment)	→	약쏙
축구 (soccer)	→	축꾸
덥다 (hot)	→	덥따
춥다 (cold)	→	춥따
욕심 (greed)	→	욕씸

Now please write down the pronunciation of the given words.

1. 국수 (noodles) → _____.

2. 닫다 (to close) → _____.

3. 속담 (proverb) → _____.

4. 잡지 (magazine) → _____.

5. 믿다 (to trust) → _____.

Considering this, we can also learn that the final consonants that should be pronounced as [ㄱ], [ㄷ], and [ㅂ] have also the same effect on the following initial consonant.

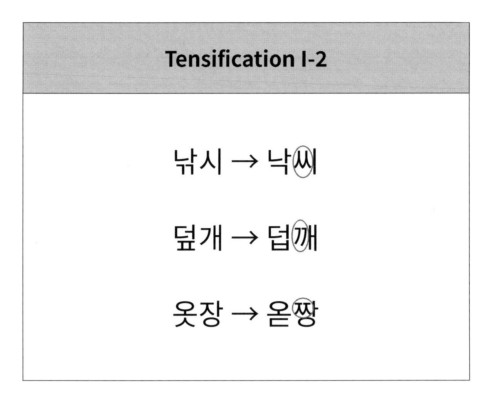

Previously, we learned the final consonants, ㄱ, ㅋ, and ㄲ, all are pronounced as [ㄱ]. Also the final ㅂ and ㅍ sound like [ㅂ], and the final ㄷ, ㅅ, ㅆ, ㅈ, ㅊ, ㅌ, and ㅎ all sound like [ㄷ]. Therefore, those consonants have the same effect on the following initial consonant when it comes to the Tensification.

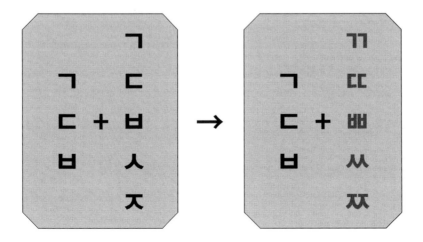

Here are some of the examples of Tensification I-2.

옆집 (next door)	→	엽찝
몇 시 (what time)	→	멷 씨
옷걸이 (coat hanger)	→	옫꺼리
늦가을 (late autumn)	→	늗까을
부엌도 (부엌: kitchen)	→	부억또
숲 속 (in the forest)	→	숩 쏙
묶다 (to tie)	→	묵따
돌솥밥 (hot pot rice)	→	돌솓빱
닦다 (to mop)	→	닥따
앞주머니 (front pocket)	→	압쭈머니

Now please write down the pronunciation of the given words.

1. 갚다 (to pay back) → _____.

2. 뒷다리 (hind leg) → _____.

3. 볶다 (to fry) → _____.

4. 꽃밭 (flower garden) → _____.

5. 밑줄 (underline) → _____.

Second, let's learn how to pronounce when the final consonants, ㄴ, ㄹ, ㅁ, ㅇ are placed before an initial consonant of the following letter.

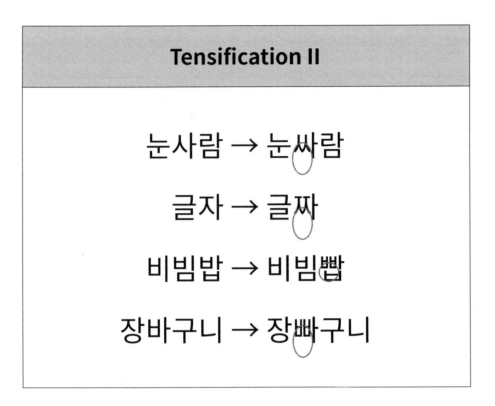

Tensification II

눈사람 → 눈싸람

글자 → 글짜

비빔밥 → 비빔빱

장바구니 → 장빠구니

When the final consonants are ㄴ, ㄹ, ㅁ, or ㅇ, and are placed before the initial consonant of the following letter, they make the following initial consonant into a tense sound.

Here are some of the examples of Tensification II.

산불 (forest fire)   →   산뿔

발등 (top of the foot)   →   발뜽

보름달 (full moon)   →   보름딸

용돈 (allowance)   →   용똔

손가락 (finger)   →   손까락

물감 (paints)   →   물깜

몸집 (physique)   →   몸찝

길가 (street)   →   길까

뺄셈 (subtraction)   →   뺄쎔

오이냉국 (cold soup with cucumber) →   오이냉꾹

Now please write down the pronunciation of the given words.

1. 물고기 (fish)   →   _____.

2. 여름밤 (summer night)   →   _____.

3. 결심 (resolution)   →   _____.

4. 무심결 (unintentionally)   →   _____.

5. 강가 (riverside)   →   _____.

Part 2

Practice 1

Choose the right pronunciation of the words given below.

1. 발자국   ① 발짜국   ② 발자국
2. 백두산   ① 백두산   ② 백뚜산
3. 손바닥   ① 손바닥   ② 손빠닥
4. 국자   ① 국짜   ② 꾹자
5. 옆구리   ① 엽꾸리   ② 옆꾸리
6. 산골짜기   ① 산골짜기   ② 산꼴짜기
7. 알림장   ① 알림짱   ② 알림장
8. 꽃집   ① 꼳집   ② 꼳찝
9. 낮잠   ① 낮짬   ② 낟짬
10. 헛수고   ① 헛쑤고   ② 헏쑤고
11. 낯설다   ① 낟썰다   ② 낟설다
12. 맵다   ① 맵다   ② 맵따
13. 새색시   ① 새색시   ② 새색씨
14. 옥수수   ① 옥쑤수   ② 옥수수
15. 백과사전   ① 백과사전   ② 백꽈사전

Practice 2

 Listen carefully to the recordings and choose the right pronunciation of the given words. Each one will be read once.

1. 핵심 ① ②

2. 책가방 ① ②

3. 물감 ① ②

4. 발자국 ① ②

5. 바람결 ① ②

6. 문득 ① ②

7. 손바닥 ① ②

8. 햇볕 ① ②

9. 맛살 ① ②

10. 낮다 ① ②

11. 높다 ① ②

12. 연못가 ① ②

13. 낱개 ① ②

14. 묶다 ① ②

15. 확산 ① ②

16. 액자 ① ②

17. 무릎도 ① ②

18. 엎드려 ① ②

19. 낙서 ① ②

20. 돌부리 ① ②

Practice 3

 Listen carefully to the recordings and fill in the blanks by writing down an appropriate letter. Each word will be read once. (Feel free to play more if you need.)

1. 탁 ☐

2. 골목 ☐

3. 책 ☐ 피

4. 백 ☐

5. 밤 ☐

6. 맵 ☐

7. 자랑 ☐ 리

8. 아침 ☐

9. 궁금 ☐

10. 밤 ☐

11. 댄 ☐

12. 활 ☐

13. 덕 ☐ 궁

14. 장난 ☐

15. 앞 ☐

16. 짚 ☐

17. 꽃 ☐ 네

18. 같 ☐

19. 곳 ☐

20. 숯 ☐

Part 3

Practice 1

Read carefully the sentences below and circle the letters that the Tensification rule can be applied. Each sentence has two answers.

1. 가을밤 숲길을 걸어요.

2. 식당에서 오징어 덮밥을 먹어요.

3. 늦잠을 자서 택시를 탔어요.

4. 옆집 사람들이 물고기를 키워요.

5. 산책 후에 강아지의 앞발을 닦다.

6. 고구마를 알맞게 굽다.

7. 낯선 사람이 옥수수를 줬어요.

8. 햇살이 밝게 비치는 창가에 앉아

9. 꽃집에는 예쁜 꽃들이 있어요.

10. 숙제를 마치고 낮잠을 자요.

11. 숨은 그림 찾기는 쉽게 해요.

12. 액자에 대한 궁금증이 풀렸어요.

13. 꽃집에 들러서 꽃 향기를 맡고

14. 갑자기 비가 내려서 각자 집으로 갔어요.

15. 산길을 걷다가 강아지를 봤어요.

Practice 2

 Listen carefully to the recordings and write down what you hear. Each one will be read once. (Feel free to play more if you need.)

1. _____ .

2. _____ .

3. _____ .

4. _____ .

5. _____ .

6. _____ .

7. _____ .

8. _____ .

9. _____ .

10. _____ .

11. _____ .

12. _____ .

13. _____ .

14. _____ .

15. _____ .

16. _____ .

17. _____ .

18. _____ .

19. _____ .

20. _____ .

제12과

발음규칙 III
Palatalization

학습목표 OBJECTIVES

✓ How to read when the final consonant ㄷ is placed before a letter with no initial consonant and ㅣ, ㅑ, ㅕ, ㅛ, ㅠ as its vowel

✓ How to read when the final consonant ㅌ is placed before a letter with no initial consonant and ㅣ, ㅑ, ㅕ, ㅛ, ㅠ as its vowel

Part 1

First, let's learn how the sounds change when the final consonant ㄷ is placed before a letter with no initial consonant and ㅣ, ㅑ, ㅕ, ㅛ, ㅠ as its vowel.

Palatalization I

해돋이 → 해돋이   ~~해도디~~

맏이 → 마지   ~~마디~~

When the final consonant ㄷ is placed before a letter with no initial consonant and ㅣ as its vowel, [ㄷ] is changed into [ㅈ].

ㄷ + 이   →   지 + ~~디~~

In theory, this phenomenon also happens when the vowel of the following letter is ㅑ, ㅕ, ㅛ, or ㅠ. However, it is very rare to find the examples of them in everyday conversations.

Second, let's learn how the sounds change when the final consonant ㅌ is placed before a letter with no initial consonant and ㅣ, ㅑ, ㅕ, ㅛ, ㅠ as its vowel.

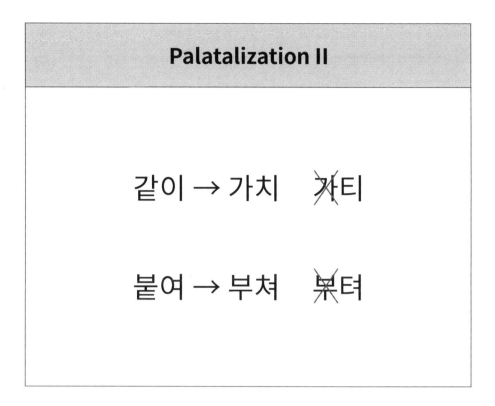

When the final consonant ㅌ is placed before a letter with no initial consonant and ㅣ, ㅑ, ㅕ, ㅛ, or ㅠ as its vowel, [ㅌ] is changed into [ㅊ].

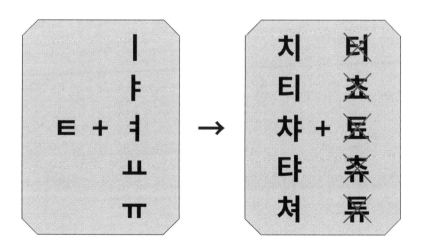

Here are some of the examples of Palatalization.

굳이 (obstinately)　　　　　　→　　　구지

미닫이 (sliding door)　　　　　→　　　미다지

가을걷이 (autumn harvest)　　→　　　가을거지

반닫이 (cabinet)　　　　　　　→　　　반다지

샅샅이 (thoroughly)　　　　　→　　　삳싸치

쇠붙이 (iron)　　　　　　　　　→　　　쇠부치

끝이 (끝: the end)　　　　　　→　　　끄치

덧붙이다 (to add)　　　　　　→　　　덛뿌치다

Now please write down the pronunciation of the given words.

1. 곧이 (straightforwardly)　　→　　_____.

2. 같이 (together)　　　　　　→　　_____.

3. 붙여 (붙이다: to attach)　　→　　_____.

4. 걸레받이 (mopboard)　　　→　　_____.

5. 걷어붙여 (걷어붙이다: to roll up)　→　_____.

Part 2

Practice 1

Choose the right pronunciation of the words given below.

1. 등받이   ① 등바지   ② 등바디

2. 여닫이   ① 여다디   ② 여다지

3. 붙여   ① 부텨   ② 부쳐

4. 가을걷이   ① 가을거지   ② 가을거디

5. 미닫이   ① 미다지   ② 미다디

6. 똑같은   ① 똑까튼   ② 똑까츤

7. 해돋이   ① 해도디   ② 해도지

8. 붙이다   ① 부치다   ② 부티다

9. 곧이   ① 고디   ② 고지

10. 끝은   ① 끄튼   ② 끄츤

11. 피붙이   ① 피부티   ② 피부치

12. 내붙였다   ① 내부쳗따   ② 내부텯따

13. 접붙이기   ① 접뿌치기   ② 접뿌티기

14. 하나같이   ① 하나가티   ② 하나가치

15. 붙어서   ① 부터서   ② 부쳐서

Practice 2

 Listen carefully to the recordings and fill in the blanks by writing down an appropriate letter. Each word will be read once. (Feel free to play more if you need.)

1. ☐ 이

2. ☐ 이

3. 미 ☐ 이

4. 삳 ☐ 이

5. 걷어 ☐ 여

6. 걸레 ☐ 이

7. 덧 ☐ 이기

8. 등 ☐ 이

9. 해 ☐ 이

10. ☐ 이

11. ☐ 이

12. ☐ 이

13. ☐ 이

14. 쏘아 ☐ 이다

15. 여 ☐ 이

Part 3

Practice 1

Read carefully the sentences below and circle the letters that the Palatalization rule can be applied. Each sentence has one answer.

1. 제가 우리 집의 맏이입니다.

2. 덧붙여서 말하자면, 이 책은 아주 유익합니다.

3. 우리 같이 불꽃놀이 보러 갈래?

4. 강아지 털을 샅샅이 뒤져서 진드기를 잡아 내다.

5. 쇠붙이는 촬영 전에 제거해야 합니다.

6. 한옥에는 여닫이 문이 많이 있다.

7. 내가 굳이 그걸 말로 해야겠니?

8. 철저한 분장으로 감쪽같이 속였다.

9. 그렇게 쏘아붙이면 기분이 어떻겠어?

10. 쪽지를 써서 벽에다 붙여야겠다.

11. 그걸 곧이곧대로 믿다니 어리석구나.

12. 지금이 한창 가을걷이할 시기야.

13. 우리 형은 내게 유일한 피붙이이다.

14. 너의 잘못을 낱낱이 말해 줄게.

15. 끝이 올 때까지 우리 모두 인내해야 한다.

Practice 2

 Listen carefully to the recordings and write down what you hear. Each one will be read once. (Feel free to play more if you need.)

1. _____ .

2. _____ .

3. _____ .

4. _____ .

5. _____ .

6. _____ .

7. _____ .

8. _____ .

9. _____ .

10. _____ .

11. _____ .

12. _____ .

13. _____ .

14. _____ .

15. _____ .

16. _____ .

17. _____ .

18. _____ .

19. _____ .

20. _____ .

제13과

발음규칙 IV
Aspirationalization

학습목표 OBJECTIVES

✓ How to read words correctly when the final consonant, [ㅎ] meets with an initial consonant of the following letter

✓ How to read words correctly when final consonants, [ㄱ], [ㄷ], [ㅂ], [ㅅ], [ㅈ] meet with [ㅎ] as an initial consonant of the following letter

Part 1

First, let's learn how to read words correctly when the final consonant, [ㅎ] meets with an initial consonant of the following letter.

Aspirationalization I

동그랗게 → 동그라케

그렇다 → 그러타

놓지 → 노치

When the final consonant, ㅎ meets with the initial consonant ㄱ, ㄷ, or ㅈ of the following letter, it is changed into [ㅋ], [ㅌ], [ㅊ] respectively.

Here are some of the examples of Aspirationalization I.

쌓지 (쌓다: to pile up) → 싸치

넣고 (넣다: to put something in) → 너코

낳다 (to give birth to) → 나타

빨갛게 (빨갛다: red) → 빨가케

이렇지 (like this) → 이러치

좋다 (good) → 조타

그렇지만 (however) → 그러치만

아무렇지 (아무렇다: whatever) → 아무러치

사이좋게 (in a good relationship) → 사이조케

놓고 (놓다: to put something on) → 노코

Now please write down the pronunciation of the given words.

1. 어떻게 (how) → _____.

2. 노랗다 (yellow) → _____.

3. 까맣지 (까맣다: black) → _____.

4. 벌겋게 (벌겋다: reddish) → _____.

5. 그렇고 (like that) → _____.

Second, let's learn how to read words correctly when final consonants, [ㄱ], [ㄷ], [ㅂ], [ㅅ], [ㅈ] meet with [ㅎ] as an initial consonant of the following letter.

Aspirationalization II

생각하다 → 생가카다

입학 → 이팍

When the final consonants, ㄱ, ㄷ, ㅂ, ㅅ, and ㅈ meets with the initial consonant ㅎ of the following letter, it is changed as below.

ㄱ
ㄷ
ㅂ + ㅎ → ㅋ
ㅅ   ㅌ / ㅊ
ㅈ   ㅍ
           ㅌ
           ㅊ / ㅌ

Be careful that the final ㄷ and the following 히 make the sound of [치] according to the Palatalization rule. Do not pronounce it as [티].

Here are some of the examples of Aspirationalization II.

기억하다 (to remember)	→	기어카다
닫히다 (to close)	→	다치다
잊혀지다 (to be forgotten)	→	이쳐지다
식혜 (Korean sweet rice punch)	→	시켸
잘못하다 (to commit an error)	→	잘모타다
낮 한때 (at one time during the day)	→	나탄때
맏형 (eldest brother)	→	마텽
뿌듯하다 (to be filled with joy)	→	뿌드타다
꽂히다 (to be into sth)	→	꼬치다
급하다 (urgent)	→	그파다

Now please write down the pronunciation of the given words.

1. 못하다 (to fail to) → _____.

2. 좁히다 (to narrow) → _____.

3. 축하해 (congratulations) → _____.

4. 박히다 (be hammered) → _____.

5. 굳히다 (to harden) → _____.

Part 2

Practice 1

Choose the right pronunciation of the words given below.

1. 맺히다   ① 매치다   ② 매티다
2. 가득히   ① 가드키   ② 가득히
3. 못해서   ① 모채서   ② 모태서
4. 쌓다   ① 싸타   ② 싸차
5. 걷히다   ① 거티다   ② 거치다
6. 노력하다   ① 노려타다   ② 노려카다
7. 답하다   ① 다파다   ② 다카다
8. 둥그렇다   ① 둥그러다   ② 둥그러타
9. 젖히다   ① 저티다   ② 저치다
10. 막히다   ① 막히다   ② 마키다
11. 솔직히   ① 솔찌키   ② 솔찌피
12. 많다   ① 만따   ② 만타
13. 밥하고   ① 바하고   ② 바파고
14. 않다   ① 안타   ② 안따
15. 좋다   ① 조따   ② 조타

Practice 2

 Listen carefully to the recordings and choose the right pronunciation of the given words. Each one will be read once.

1. 어둑한   ① ②

2. 아무렇게나   ① ②

3. 잊히다   ① ②

4. 걷히다   ① ②

5. 꽂힌   ① ②

6. 막혀   ① ②

7. 닫힌다   ① ②

8. 입히다   ① ②

9. 많다   ① ②

10. 막히다   ① ②

11. 좁히다   ① ②

12. 답하시오   ① ②

13. 가득하다   ① ②

14. 묻히다   ① ②

15. 뿌듯하다   ① ②

16. 못해   ① ②

17. 그렇지만   ① ②

18. 어떻게   ① ②

19. 놓고   ① ②

20. 잊혀   ① ②

Practice 3

 Listen carefully to the recordings and fill in the blanks by writing down an appropriate letter. Each word will be read once. (Feel free to play more if you need.)

1. 행 ☐ 해

2. 잡 ☐ 다

3. ☐ 학

4. ☐ 혜

5. 맏 ☐

6. 묻 ☐ 다

7. 맺 ☐ 다

8. 닫 ☐ 다

9. 어떻 ☐

10. ☐ 기로

11. 넝 ☐

12. 이렇 ☐

13. 곱다 ☐ 게

14. ☐ 다

15. 둥그 ☐ 게

16. 그 ☐ 지

17. 좋 ☐ 만

18. 많 ☐

19. 노랗 ☐

20. 가 ☐ 하다

Part 3

Practice 1

Read carefully the sentences below and circle the letters that the Aspirationalization rule can be applied. Each sentence has one answer.

1. 단풍잎으로 거리가 울긋불긋하게 변했다.

2. 성격이 급해서 차분해지는 연습을 한다.

3. 잎사귀에 이슬이 맺혔다.

4. 그렇게 말하는 이유는 뭐야?

5. 노력하는 사람이 멋있다.

6. 강아지에게 옷을 입혔다.

7. 코가 막혀서 목소리가 제대로 안 나와요.

8. 발에 물집이 잡혀서 뛸 수가 없어요.

9. 졸업과 입학의 계절이 왔어요.

10. 잘못한 일에 대해서는 사과를 해야죠.

11. 언제나 정직하게 행동하는 게 중요해요.

12. 한국 사람은 아침에 밥하고 국을 먹어야 해요.

13. 제일 무서운 것은 잊혀지는 거야.

14. 둥그렇게 둘러 앉아서 밤새도록 얘기를 나누다.

15. 대문이 쿵 하고 닫혔다.

Practice 2

 Listen carefully to the recordings and write down what you hear. Each one will be read once. (Feel free to play more if you need.)

1. _____   _____ .

2. _____ .

3. _____ .

4. _____ .

5. _____ .

6. _____ .

7. _____ .

8. _____ .

9. _____ .

10. _____ .

11. _____ .

12. _____ .

13. _____ .

14. _____ .

15. _____ .

16. _____ .

17. _____ .

18. _____ .

19. _____ .

20. _____ .

제14과

발음규칙 V
Consonant Assimilation

학습목표 OBJECTIVES

✓ How to read words correctly when the final consonants, ㄱ, ㄲ, ㅋ meet with initial consonants, ㄴ, ㄹ, ㅁ of the following letter

✓ How to read words correctly when final consonants, [ㄷ] (ㄷ, ㅅ, ㅆ, ㅈ, ㅊ, ㅌ), [ㅂ] (ㅂ, ㅍ) meet with ㄴ, ㄹ, ㅁ as an initial consonant of the following letter

✓ How to read words correctly when the final consonants, ㄴ, ㄹ, ㅁ, ㅇ meet with initial consonants, ㄴ, ㄹ of the following letter

Part 1

First, let's learn how to read words correctly when the final consonants, ㄱ, ㄲ, ㅋ meet with initial consonants, ㄴ, ㅁ of the following letter.

Consonant Assimilation I

막내 → 망내

국물 → 궁물

When the final consonants, ㄱ, ㄲ, ㅋ meet with the initial consonants ㄴ or ㅁ of the following letter, ㄱ, ㄲ, ㅋ are changed into [ㅇ].

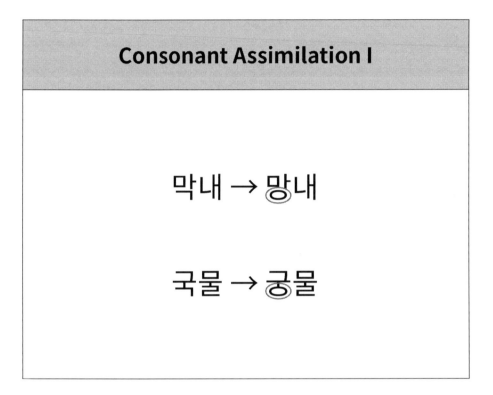

Here are some of the examples of Consonant Assimilation I.

식물 (plant)   →   싱물

볶는다 (볶다: to fry)   →   봉는다

부엌문 (kitchen door)   →   부엉문

악몽 (nightmare)   →   앙몽

숙녀 (lady)   →   숭녀

묶는다 (묶다: to tie)   →   뭉는다

속눈썹 (eyelashes)   →   송눈썹

먹는 (먹다: to eat)   →   멍는

국물 (soup)   →   궁물

막내 (the youngest)   →   망내

Now please write down the pronunciation of the given words.

1. 고객님 (customer)   →   _____.

2. 학문 (studies)   →   _____

3. 낚는다 (낚다: to hook)   →   _____

4. 박물관 (museum)   →   _____

5. 속마음 (one's innermost feelings) →   _____

Second, let's learn how to read words correctly when the final consonants, [ㄷ] (ㄷ, ㅅ, ㅆ, ㅈ, ㅊ, ㅌ), [ㅂ] (ㅂ, ㅍ) meet with initial consonants, ㄴ, ㅁ of the following letter.

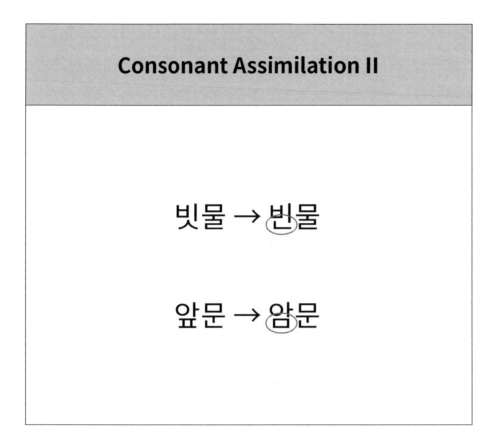

Consonant Assimilation II

빗물 → 빈물

앞문 → 암문

When the final consonants, [ㄷ] (ㄷ, ㅅ, ㅆ, ㅈ, ㅊ, ㅌ), [ㅂ] (ㅂ, ㅍ) meet with initial consonants, ㄴ, ㅁ of the following letter, [ㄷ] is changed into [ㄴ], and [ㅂ] into [ㅁ].

ㄷ + ㄴ → ㄴ + ㄴ
ㅂ   ㅁ   ㅁ   ㅁ

Here are some of the examples of Consonant Assimilation II.

낱말 (word)   →   난말

콧물 (nasal discharge)   →   콘물

빛나다 (to shine)   →   빈나다

십 년 (ten years)   →   심년

앞머리 (bangs)   →   암머리

첫눈 (first snow)   →   천눈

짖는 (짖다: to bark)   →   진는

밥맛 (appetite)   →   밤맏

빗물 (rainwater)   →   빈물

앞문 (front door)   →   암문

Now please write down the pronunciation of the given words.

1. 꽃눈 (flower bud)   →   _____.

2. 거짓말 (lies)   →   _____.

3. 앞니 (front teeth)   →   _____.

4. 겉모양 (appearance)   →   _____.

5. 믿는다 (믿다: to trust)   →   _____.

Next, let's learn how to read words correctly when the final consonants, [ㄱ] (ㄱ, ㄲ, ㅋ), [ㄷ] (ㄷ, ㅅ, ㅆ, ㅈ, ㅊ, ㅌ), [ㅂ] (ㅂ, ㅍ) meet with initial consonants, ㄹ of the following letter.

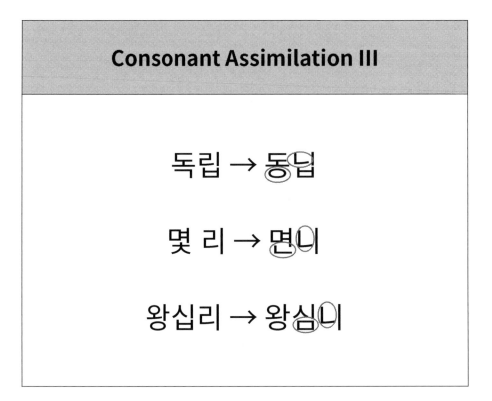

When the final consonants, [ㄱ] (ㄱ, ㄲ, ㅋ), [ㄷ] (ㄷ, ㅅ, ㅆ, ㅈ, ㅊ, ㅌ), and [ㅂ] (ㅂ, ㅍ) meet with the initial consonant ㄹ of the following letter, [ㄱ] is changed into [ㅇ], [ㄷ] into [ㄴ], and [ㅂ] into [ㅁ]. Also, ㄹ of the following letter is changed into [ㄴ].

Here are some of the examples of Consonant Assimilation III.

협력 (cooperation)   →   혐녁

국립 (national)   →   궁닙

백로 (white heron)   →   뱅노

속력 (speed)   →   송녁

압력 (pressure)   →   암녁

섭리 (providence)   →   섬니

식량 (food)   →   싱냥

법률 (law)   →   범뉼

독립 (independence)   →   동닙

육류 (meat)   →   융뉴

Now please write down the pronunciation of the given words.

1. 국력 (national power)   →   _____.

2. 측량 (measurement)   →   _____.

3. 입력 (input)   →   _____.

4. 속리산 (Mt. Songni)   →   _____.

5. 급류 (torrent)   →   _____.

Next, let's learn how to read words correctly when the final consonants, ㅁ and ㅇ meet with the initial consonant, ㄹ of the following letter.

Consonant Assimilation IV

음료수 → 음뇨수

승리 → 승니

When the final consonants, ㅁ and ㅇ meet with the initial consonant, ㄹ of the following letter, the following ㄹ is changed into [ㄴ].

ㅁ
ㅇ + ㄹ → ㅁ
ㅇ + ㄴ

Here are some of the examples of Consonant Assimilation IV.

왕릉 (royal mausoleum)   →   왕능

심리 (psychology)   →   심니

음료수 (beverage)   →   음뇨수

승리 (victory)   →   승니

대통령 (president)   →   대통녕

정류장 (bus stop, station)   →   정뉴장

상류 (upper region)   →   상뉴

공룡 (dinosaur)   →   공뇽

영리하다 (to be clever)   →   영니하다

강력하다 (to be powerful)   →   강녀카다

Now please write down the pronunciation of the given words.

1. 장롱 (wardrobe)   → _____.

2. 종로 (Jongno – a district in Seoul)   → _____.

3. 담력 (courage)   → _____.

4. 강릉 (Gangneung – a city in Korea)   → _____.

5. 침략 (invasion)   → _____.

Lastly, let's learn how to read words correctly when ㄴ and ㄹ and vice versa meet as a final consonant of a previous letter and an initial consonant of a following letter.

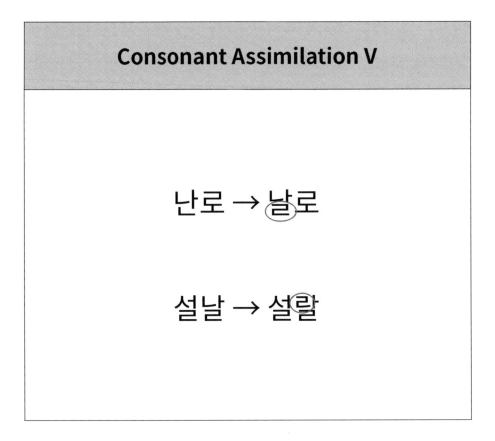

When ㄴ and ㄹ and vice versa meet as a final consonant of a previous letter and an initial consonant of a following letter, those two consonants are turned into [ㄹ].

Here are some of the examples of Consonant assimilation V.

편리 (convenience) → 펼리

줄넘기 (jump rope) → 줄럼끼

인류 (humankind) → 일류

훈련 (training) → 훌련

한류 (Korean Wave) → 할류

일 년 (one year) → 일련

난로 (stove) → 날로

설날 (Lunar New Year's Day) → 설랄

연락 (contact) → 열락

진로 (career path) → 질로

Now please write down the pronunciation of the given words.

1. 달님 (Moon) → _____.

2. 원리 (principle) → _____.

3. 단락 (paragraph) → _____.

4. 신랑 (bridegroom) → _____.

5. 분류 (classification) → _____.

Part 2

Practice 1

Choose the right pronunciation of the words given below.

1. 목마르다   ① 몽마르다   ② 몬마르다

2. 입는   ① 임는   ② 임른

3. 목례   ① 몽례   ② 몽녜

4. 경로당   ① 경로당   ② 경노당

5. 물난리   ① 문난리   ② 물랄리

6. 학년   ① 항년   ② 항련

7. 콧날   ① 콘랄   ② 콘날

8. 압력   ① 암력   ② 암녁

9. 상륙하다   ① 상류카다   ② 상뉴카다

10. 간략하게   ① 간냐카게   ② 갈랴카게

11. 꺾는다   ① 꺽른다   ② 껑는다

12. 윷놀이   ① 윤노리   ② 윤노리

13. 협력   ① 혐력   ② 혐녁

14. 궁리하다   ① 궁니하다   ② 궁리하다

15. 오늘날   ① 오를랄   ② 오늘랄

Practice 2

 Listen carefully to the recordings and choose the right pronunciation of the given words. Each one will be read once.

1. 막내   ① ②
2. 폭로   ① ②
3. 씻는   ① ②
4. 법률   ① ②
5. 신라   ① ②
6. 육류   ① ②
7. 식량   ① ②
8. 입맛   ① ②
9. 속리산   ① ②
10. 한라산   ① ②

11. 숙모   ① ②
12. 박람회   ① ②
13. 꽃무늬   ① ②
14. 협력   ① ②
15. 종로   ① ②
16. 먹는다   ① ②
17. 독립   ① ②
18. 맞먹다   ① ②
19. 맛있는   ① ②
20. 이튿날   ① ②

Practice 3

 Listen carefully to the recordings and fill in the blanks by writing down an appropriate letter. Each word will be read once. (Feel free to play more if you need.)

1. 음 ☐ 수

2. ☐ 로

3. ☐ 내

4. 앞 ☐

5. ☐ 년

6. ☐ 룡

7. ☐ 류

8. 박 ☐ 관

9. ☐ 물

10. ☐ 력

11. ☐ 리

12. 연 ☐

13. ☐ 녀

14. 속 ☐ 썹

15. ☐ 눈

16. ☐ 날

17. ☐ 로

18. 악 ☐

19. ☐ 물

20. ☐ 놀이

Part 3

Practice 1

Read carefully the sentences below and circle the letters that the Consonant Assimilation rule can be applied. Each sentence has one answer.

1. 오늘은 왠지 입맛이 없다.

2. 제가 끝마무리를 할게요.

3. 지금 우리 차에 짐을 싣는 중이에요.

4. 강아지가 폴짝폴짝 걷는다.

5. 가을에는 서울에서 불꽃놀이 축제가 열린다.

6. 이튿날이 되자 날씨가 맑아졌다.

7. 그 사람한테서 연락이 오지 않아요.

8. 시민들이 강력하게 항의한다.

9. 경로당에 아무도 안 계시네요.

10. 종로3가에서 지하철 3호선을 타세요.

11. 원리를 알면 수학이 쉽다.

12. 이건 한국말로 뭐라고 해요?

13. 그럴 땐 "감사합니다"라고 말해요.

14. 내년에 대통령 선거가 있어요.

15. 오늘날 사람들은 바쁘게 살고 있다.

Practice 2

 Listen carefully to the recordings and write down what you hear. Each one will be read once. (Feel free to play more if you need.)

1. _____.

2. _____.

3. _____.

4. _____.

5. _____.

6. _____.

7. _____.

8. _____.

9. _____.

10. _____.

11. _____.

12. _____.

13. _____.

14. _____.

15. _____.

16. _____.

17. _____.

18. _____.

19. _____.

20. _____.

제 15 과

발음규칙 VI
Phoneme Addition

학습목표 OBJECTIVES

✓ How to read words correctly when the previous word of a compound word ends with a final consonant and the following word starts with ㅣ, ㅑ, ㅕ, ㅛ, ㅠ without an initial consonant

✓ How to read words correctly when the previous word of a compound word ends with ㄹ and the following word starts with ㅣ, ㅑ, ㅕ, ㅛ, ㅠ without an initial consonant

✓ How to read words correctly when a word is followed by another word starting with ㅣ, ㅑ, ㅕ, ㅛ, ㅠ without an initial consonant

Part 1

First, let's learn how to read words correctly when the previous word of a compound word ends with a final consonant and the following word starts with ㅣ, ㅑ, ㅕ, ㅛ, ㅠ without an initial consonant

Phoneme Addition I
단풍잎 (단풍 + 잎) → 단풍닙 한여름 (한 + 여름) → 한녀름

When the previous word of a compound word ends with a final consonant and the following word starts with ㅣ, ㅑ, ㅕ, ㅛ, ㅠ without an initial consonant, additional [ㄴ] is inserted.

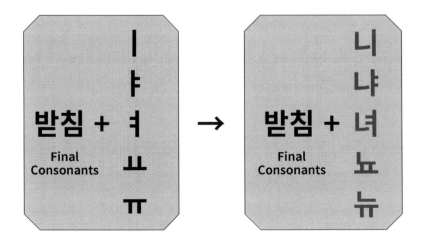

Here are some of the examples of Phoneme Addition I.

담요 (담+요: blanket) → 담뇨

꽃잎 (꽃+잎: flower petal) → 꼰닙

색연필 (색+연필: colored pencil) → 생년필

단풍잎 (단풍+잎: tinged autumnal leaf) → 단풍닙

식용유 (식용+유: cooking oil) → 시공뉴

앞일 (앞+일: one's future) → 암닐

태평양 (태평+양: the Pacific Ocean) → 태평냥

배낭여행 (배낭+여행: backpacking) → 배낭녀행

한여름 (한+여름: midsummer) → 한녀름

솜이불 (솜+이불: cotton comforter) → 솜니불

Now please write down the pronunciation of the given words.

1. 학생용 (학생+용: for students) → _____.

2. 정열 (정+열: passion) → _____.

3. 부엌일 (부엌+일: to hook) → _____.

4. 맨입 (맨+입: an empty mouth) → _____.

5. 막일 (막+일: manual labor) → _____.

Second, let's learn how to read words correctly when the previous word of a compound word ends with ㄹ and the following word starts with ㅣ, ㅑ, ㅕ, ㅛ, ㅠ without an initial consonant.

Phoneme Addition II

서울역 (서울 + 역) → 서울력

휘발유 (휘발 + 유) → 휘발류

When the previous word of a compound word ends with ㄹ and the following word starts with ㅣ, ㅑ, ㅕ, ㅛ, ㅠ without an initial consonant, additional [ㄹ] is inserted.

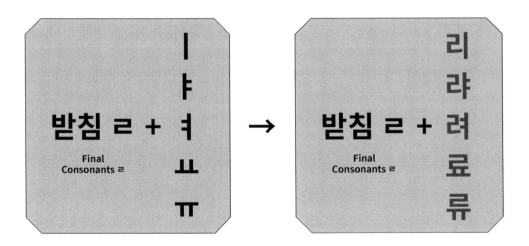

Here are some of the examples of Phoneme Addition II.

알약 (알+약: tablet, pill)　　　　　→　　알략

올여름 (올+여름: this summer)　　　→　　올려름

풀잎 (풀+잎: blade of grass)　　　　→　　풀립

서울역 (서울+역: Seoul Station)　　→　　서울력

지하철역 (지하철+역: subway station) →　지하철력

휘발유 (휘발+유: gasoline)　　　　　→　　휘발류

설익다 (설+익다: to be half-cooked)　→　　설릭따

볼일 (볼+일: business, things to do)　→　　볼릴

돌이끼 (돌+이끼: moss on a rock)　　→　　돌리끼

떡갈나무 (떡갈+나무: oak tree)　　　→　　떡깔라무

Now please write down the pronunciation of the given words.

1. 물약 (물+약: liquid medicine)　　→　_____.

2. 연료 (연+료: fuel)　　　　　　　→　_____.

3. 길옆 (길+옆: roadside)　　　　　→　_____.

4. 솔잎 (솔+잎: pine needles)　　　→　_____.

5. 불여우 (불+여우: vixen)　　　　→　_____.

Lastly, the two rules can also be applied when a word is followed by another word starting with ㅣ, ㅑ, ㅕ, ㅛ, ㅠ without an initial consonant. Here are some of the examples.

깨진 유리 (broken glass)	→	깨진 뉴리
더운 여름 (hot summer)	→	더운 녀름
예쁜 여자 (beautiful woman)	→	예쁜 녀자
할 일 (things to do)	→	할 릴
신나는 야구 (exciting baseball game)	→	신나는 냐구
무서운 이야기 (scary story)	→	무서운 니야기
맛있는 요리 (delicious food)	→	마신는 뇨리
어려운 일 (difficult job)	→	어려운 닐
나는 연 (flying kite)	→	나는 년
발굴할 유물 (relics to be excavated)	→	발구랄 류물

Now please write down the pronunciation of the given words.

1. 힘든 일 (tricky job) → _____.

2. 할 이야기 (story to talk about) → _____.

3. 결혼할 여자 (woman to marry) → _____.

4. 깨끗한 유리 (clear glass) → _____.

5. 쉬운 역할 (easy job) → _____.

Part 2

Practice 1

Choose the right pronunciation of the words given below.

1. 색연필   ① 생년필   ② 새견필

2. 물약   ① 물략   ② 무략

3. 힘든 일   ① 힘드닐   ② 힘든닐

4. 단풍잎   ① 단푼닙   ② 단풍닙

5. 휘발유   ① 휘발류   ② 휘바류

6. 신나는 이야기   ① 신나는니야기   ② 신나느니야기

7. 태평양   ① 태평냥   ② 태평량

8. 올여름   ① 올려름   ② 올녀름

9. 착한 여자   ① 차칸녀자   ② 차카녀자

10. 집안일   ① 지바닐   ② 지반닐

11. 길옆   ① 길렵   ② 기렵

12. 영리한 여우   ① 영리하녀우   ② 영리한녀우

13. 한여름   ① 한녀름   ② 한려름

14. 풀잎   ① 풀닙   ② 풀립

15. 발굴할 유물   ① 발구랄뉴물   ② 발구랄류물

Practice 2

 Listen carefully to the recordings and choose the right pronunciation of the given words. Each one will be read once.

1. 열여섯 ① ②

2. 담요 ① ②

3. 무슨 일 ① ②

4. 스물여덟 ① ②

5. 앞일 ① ②

6. 깨진 유리 ① ②

7. 서른여섯 ① ②

8. 물약 ① ②

9. 예쁜 여자 ① ②

10. 쌀엿 ① ②

11. 서울역 ① ②

12. 나는 연 ① ②

13. 떡잎 ① ②

14. 돌이끼 ① ②

15. 힘든 일 ① ②

16. 정열 ① ②

17. 일일이 ① ②

18. 볼일 ① ②

19. 배낭여행 ① ②

20. 화낼 일 ① ②

Practice 3

Listen carefully to the recordings and fill in the blanks by writing down an appropriate letter. Each word will be read once. (Feel free to play more if you need.)

1. 깨진 □ 리

2. 단풍 □

3. 맛있는 □ 리

4. 무더운 □ 름

5. 배낭 □ 행

6. 색 □ 필

7. 서울 □

8. 신나는 □ 구

9. 알 □

10. 앞 □

11. 어려운 □

12. 열 □ 섯

13. 올 □ 름

14. 일 □ 이

15. 지하철 □

16. 착한 □

17. 풀 □

18. 한국 □ 사

19. 할 □ 야기

20. 휘발 □

Part 3

Practice 1

Read carefully the sentences below and circle the letters that the Phoneme Addition rule can be applied. Each sentence has one answer.

1. 식용유로 볶으면 맛이 좋아요.

2. 내일은 할 일이 많아서 만날 수 없어요.

3. 색연필과 종이만 있으면 누구나 가능해요.

4. 비행기를 타고 태평양을 건너 갑니다.

5. 엄마는 집안일 하시느라 바쁘세요.

6. 한여름에는 집에 있는 게 최고다.

7. 중요한 정보를 맨입으로 알아내려고 하는 거니?

8. 가을에는 길옆에 코스모스가 예쁘게 핀다.

9. 보통 힘든 일을 맡으면 거절을 못한다.

10. 내 동생은 열여섯 살이에요.

11. 맛있는 요리를 먹으면 기분이 좋아져요.

12. 이건 어차피 퍼질 이야기예요.

13. 너의 머리 스타일에 무슨 일이 생긴 거야?

14. 다행히도 이번에는 쉬운 역할을 맡았어요.

15. 아침에는 풀잎에 이슬이 맺혀 있어요.

Practice 2

 Listen carefully to the recordings and write down what you hear. Each one will be read once. (Feel free to play more if you need.)

1. _____.

2. _____.

3. _____.

4. _____.

5. _____.

6. _____.

7. _____.

8. _____.

9. _____.

10. _____.

11. _____.

12. _____.

13. _____.

14. _____.

15. _____.

16. _____.

17. _____.

18. _____.

19. _____.

20. _____.

제16과

발음규칙 VII
Sai-Sori Phenomenon

학습목표 OBJECTIVES

✓ How to read compound words correctly when inserted ㅅ(Shiot) is placed before a word that starts with ㄱ, ㄷ, ㅂ, ㅅ, ㅈ

✓ How to read compound words correctly when inserted ㅅ(Shiot) is placed before a word that starts with ㄴ, ㅁ

✓ How to read compound words correctly when inserted ㅅ(Shiot) is placed before a word that starts with a vowel and no initial consonant

Part 1

When more than two words are combined to make a compound word, ㅅ is inserted between the two. This is called Sai-Sori Phenomenon. In this book, let's focus on how to pronounce them rather than the principle of when to insert ㅅ.

First, let's learn how to read compound words correctly when inserted ㅅ is placed before a word that starts with ㄱ, ㄷ, ㅂ, ㅅ, ㅈ.

Sai-Sori Phenomenon I

바닷가: 바닫 + 가 → 바닫까

빗소리: 빋 + 소리 → 빋쏘리

As you can see above, the inserted ㅅ as a final consonant sounds like [ㄷ], so that it tensifies the following initial consonants, ㄱ, ㄷ, ㅂ, ㅅ, ㅈ. This is what we have already learned in Unit 11, Tensification I.

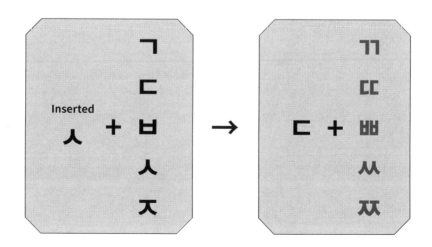

Here are some of the examples of Sai-Sori Phenomenon I.

냇가 (streamside, riverside)　　→　　낻까

햇볕 (sunlight)　　→　　핻뻗

머릿속 (in one's head)　　→　　머릳쏙

외갓집 (home of one's mother)　　→　　외갇찝

고깃국 (meat soup)　　→　　고긷꾹

촛불 (candlelight)　　→　　촏뿔

이삿짐 (packages for moving)　　→　　이삳찜

바닷가 (beach)　　→　　바닫까

빗소리 (sound of rain)　　→　　빋쏘리

깃발 (flag)　　→　　긷빨

Now please write down the pronunciation of the given words.

1. 찻잔 (teacup)　　→　　_____.

2. 기찻길 (railroad)　　→　　_____.

3. 나뭇가지 (branch of trees)　　→　　_____.

4. 전봇대 (utility pole)　　→　　_____.

5. 빗방울 (raindrop)　　→　　_____.

Second, let's learn how to read compound words correctly when inserted ㅅ is placed before a word that starts with ㄴ, ㅁ.

Sai-Sori Phenomenon II

옛날: 옏 + 날 → 옌날

수돗물: 수돋 + 물 → 수돈물

As you can see above, the inserted ㅅ as a final consonant sounds like [ㄷ], and the following ㄴ, ㅁ change [ㄷ] into [ㄴ] according to Consonant Assimilation II, which we learned in Unit 14.

Inserted ㅅ + ㄴ/ㅁ → ㄴ + ㄴ/ㅁ

Here are some of the examples of Sai-Sori Phenomenon II.

옛날 (old days) → 옌날

수돗물 (tap water) → 수돈물

아랫니 (lower teeth) → 아랜니

노랫말 (lyrics) → 노랜말

잇몸 (gum) → 인몸

빗물 (rainwater) → 빈물

뒷문 (rear door) → 뒨문

냇물 (stream, creek) → 낸물

혼잣말 (soliloquy) → 혼잔말

존댓말 (honorific expression) → 존댄말

Now please write down the pronunciation of the given words.

1. 훗날 (future) → _____.

2. 바닷물 (seawater) → _____.

3. 콧날 (nose ridge) → _____.

4. 진딧물 (aphid) → _____.

5. 윗눈썹 (upper eyelashes) → _____.

Lastly, let's learn how to read compound words correctly when inserted ㅅ is placed before a word that starts with a vowel and no initial consonant.

Sai-Sori Phenomenon III

깻잎: 깯 + 입 → 깬닙

윗입술: 윋 + 입쑬 → 윈닙쑬

As you can see above, when inserted ㅅ is placed before a word that starts with a vowel and no initial consonant, it affects both the final consonant of the previous word and the initial consonant of the following word, making both of them [ㄴ].

Inserted ㅅ + NO INITIAL CONSONANT → ㄴ + ㄴ

Here are some of the examples of Sai-Sori Phenomenon III.

깻잎 (perilla leaf)   →   깬닙

윗입술 (upper lip)   →   윈닙쑬

나뭇잎 (foliage, leaf)   →   나문닙

뒷일 (future affairs)   →   뒨닐

허드렛일 (chores)   →   허드렌닐

숫양 (ram)   →   순냥

아랫입술 (lower lip)   →   아랜닙쑬

예삿일 (trivial matter)   →   예산닐

고춧잎 (pepper leaf)   →   고춘닙

숫염소 (billy goat)   →   순념소

Now please write down the pronunciation of the given words.

1. 배춧잎 (cabbage leaf)   →   _____.

2. 담뱃잎 (tobacco leaf)   →   _____.

3. 베갯잇 (pillowcase)   →   _____.

4. 옛일 (past affairs)   →   _____.

5. 뒷입맛 (aftertaste)   →   _____.

Part 2

Practice 1

Choose the right pronunciation of the words given below.

1. 숫양   ① 순냥   ② 수댱

2. 옛날   ① 옌날   ② 옐날

3. 촛불   ① 촏뿔   ② 촌불

4. 아랫입술   ① 아래딥쑬   ② 아랜닙쑬

5. 뒷문   ① 뒏문   ② 뒤문

6. 깃발   ① 긷빨   ② 긷발

7. 뒷일   ① 뒌닐   ② 뒤딜

8. 혼잣말   ① 혼잗말   ② 혼잔말

9. 빗소리   ① 빋쏘리   ② 빋소리

10. 나뭇잎   ① 나무닙   ② 나문닙

11. 존댓말   ① 존댄말   ② 존대말

12. 이삿짐   ① 이사짐   ② 이사찜

13. 고춧잎   ① 고춘닙   ② 고추닙

14. 아랫니   ① 아랜니   ② 아래니

15. 냇가   ① 낻까   ② 낻가

Practice 2

 Listen carefully to the recordings and choose the right pronunciation of the given words. Each one will be read once.

1. 찻잔 ① ②
2. 콧날 ① ②
3. 뒷입맛 ① ②
4. 전봇대 ① ②
5. 진딧물 ① ②
6. 머릿속 ① ②
7. 기찻길 ① ②
8. 윗눈썹 ① ②
9. 외갓집 ① ②
10. 빗방울 ① ②

11. 배춧잎 ① ②
12. 고깃국 ① ②
13. 나뭇가지 ① ②
14. 담뱃잎 ① ②
15. 노랫말 ① ②
16. 훗날 ① ②
17. 베갯잇 ① ②
18. 아랫니 ① ②
19. 바닷물 ① ②
20. 옛일 ① ②

Practice 3

 Listen carefully to the recordings and fill in the blanks by writing down an appropriate letter. Each word will be read once. (Feel free to play more if you need.)

1. 존 [ ] 말

2. [ ] 몸

3. 옛 [ ]

4. 허드렛 [ ]

5. 아 [ ] 입술

6. 나 [ ] 잎

7. 수돗 [ ]

8. 햇 [ ]

9. 바 [ ] 가

10. [ ] 소리

11. 빗 [ ] 울

12. 찻 [ ]

13. [ ] 날

14. [ ] 눈썹

15. 배 [ ] 잎

16. 숫 [ ] 소

17. 바닷 [ ]

18. 기찻 [ ]

19. 전봇 [ ]

20. 혼 [ ] 말

Part 3

Practice 1

Read carefully the sentences below and circle the letters that the inserted ㅅ rule can be applied. Each sentence has one answer.

1. 이 요리는 뒷입맛이 좋지 않다.

2. 눈물이 밤새 베갯잇을 적셨다.

3. 김치 양념을 배춧잎에 버무립니다.

4. 너무 건조해서 아랫입술이 부르텄어요.

5. 그럴 땐 시쳇말로 대박이라고 하죠.

6. 옛날에 그런 얘기가 돌았죠.

7. 사람들은 더 이상 수돗물을 그대로 마시지 않아요.

8. 우리 꼬물이는 윗눈썹이 매력 포인트야.

9. 너무 바쁘고 힘들어서 혼잣말이 저절로 나온다.

10. 세숫물을 받아 놓고서 씻지 못했네.

11. 꼬물이가 뒷발차기를 할 때 너무 귀여워요.

12. 화분에 진딧물이 너무 많아요.

13. 소문난 잔칫상에 먹을 게 없다더니.

14. 너무 열심히 일해서 혓바늘이 돋았어요.

15. 쌀밥에 고깃국이면 충분하죠.

Practice 2

 Listen carefully to the recordings and write down what you hear. Each one will be read once. (Feel free to play more if you need.)

1. _____.

2. _____.

3. _____.

4. _____.

5. _____.

6. _____.

7. _____.

8. _____.

9. _____.

10. _____.

11. _____.

12. _____.

13. _____.

14. _____.

15. _____.

16. _____.

17. _____.

18. _____.

19. _____.

20. _____.

FINAL CHECK UP
(UNIT 1 – UNIT 16)

Practice 1

Below are some of the signages you can easily find in Korea. Read the Hangul letters on them.

1.

공 사 중

3.

금연구역
NO SMOKING

2.

당
기
세
요

PULL

미
세
요

PUSH

고
정
문

FIXED

4.

어린이
보호구역
천천히

Practice 2

 Listen carefully to the recordings, and choose the appropriate answers.

1. 공 / 콩 / 꽁

2. 태우다 / 데우다 / 때우다

3. 차다 / 짜다 / 자다

4. 불 / 뿔 / 풀

5. 시름 / 씨름

6. 달 / 딸 / 탈

7. 보송보송 / 뽀송뽀송 / 포근포근

8. 가지 / 까치 / 카센터

9. 딩동댕 / 땡땡땡 / 탱글탱글

10. 주물럭주물럭 / 쭈글쭈글 / 차근차근

11. 부리 / 뿌리 / 푸르다

12. 장구 / 창구 / 짱구

13. 발찌 / 팔찌 / 빨강

14. 소곤소곤 / 쌔근쌔근

15. 가오리 / 까마귀 / 머리카락

Practice 3

 Listen carefully to the recordings and write down what you hear. Each one will be read once. (Feel free to play more if you need.)

1. _____ .

2. _____ .

3. _____ .

4. _____ .

5. _____ .

6. _____ .

7. _____ .

8. _____ .

9. _____ .

10. _____ .

11. _____ .

12. _____ .

13. _____ .

14. _____ .

15. _____ .

16. _____ .

17. _____ .

18. _____ .

19. _____ .

20. _____ .

CONCLUSION AND RECOMMENDATIONS

Congratulations on making it to the end of this book! Now you have completed one of the most important parts of Korean learning. Just knowing how to read and write Hangul can give you great confidence in your Korean learning.

Some of you might have finished this book within quite a short time, and others might have studied with this book for a longer time. Whatever the case, this book is good to consult after you move on to higher levels of Korean learning. What about taking advantage of this book in the following three ways?

1. Come back and consult the part of the pronunciation rules of this book whenever you want to learn how to read new words or phrases. To get familiar with the pronunciation rules and make them your own, you need constant practice with accuracy. It is recommended that you come back to this book to check on them as often as possible.

2. Pay attention to the words included in this book. The practices and examples in this book present us with common everyday words that native Koreans frequently use. Therefore, this book serves as a vocabulary book as well as a workbook that teaches how to read and write Hangul.

3. Do not miss out on checking footnotes. This book is designed especially for those who start to learn Hangul and Korean, so we tried to simplify the complicated rules and explanations. However, just as all the other languages in the world, there are many exceptions to rules and differences from your mother tongue. We have added explanations on them in the footnotes for those who want to study further, and if you check on them you will be better at reading and writing Hangul.

From now on, you will definitely have more chances of having to read and write Hangul, since you can see as much as you know. And we expect you to read and write Hangul without hesitation and with great confidence based on what you have learned in this book!

ANSWER KEY

UNIT 1

Part 2

Practice 1

1. 1
2. 2
3. 2
4. 2
5. 1
6. 2
7. 2
8. 1
9. 2
10. 2
11. 3
12. 2
13. 4
14. 3
15. 3

Practice 2

1. ㅗ of 노
2. ㅜ of 우
3. ㅏ of 아
4. ㅓ of 어, ㅓ of 머
5. ㅓ of 저
6. ㅜ of 주
7. ㅡ of 음
8. ㅗ of 모
9. ㅗ of 봄

10. ㅡ of 름
11. ㅏ of 가
12. ㅜ of 울

Part 3

Practice 1

1. 어
2. 우
3. 아
4. 이
5. 으
6. 우아
7. 오이
8. 어이
9. 아이
10. 어우

Practice 2

1. ㅗ of 꼬
2. ㅏ of 아, 장
3. ㅓ of 엉
4. ㅣ of 기
5. ㅗ of 조
6. ㅡ of 늘
7. ㅏ of 당, 탕
8. ㅗ of 쪽
9. ㅓ of 헐, 렁
10. ㅡ of 스

UNIT 2

Part 2

Practice 1

1. 2
2. 1
3. 1
4. 1
5. 2
6. 2
7. 3
8. 3
9. 1
10. 3
11. 3
12. 3
13. 3
14. 3
15. 2

Practice 2

1. 다
2. 구
3. 노
4. 러
5. 므
6. 기
7. 루
8. 무
9. 드
10. 너
11. 구두

12. 나라

13. 나무

14. 다리

15. 다리미

16. 라디오

17. 고기

18. 노루

19. 오리

20. 우리

Part 3

Practice 1

1. 가나

2. 노루

3. 누가

4. 거기

5. 아이

6. 고무

7. 아기

8. 오이

9. 가구

10. 구리

Practice 2

1. ㄱ of 기

2. ㄴ of 늘

3. ㄱ of 공

4. ㄹ of 리

5. ㄷ of 들

6. ㅁ of 만, 남

7. ㄷ of 도

8. ㄹ of 르

9. ㄷ of 드

10. ㅁ of 물

UNIT 3

Part 2

Practice 1

1. 2

2. 1

3. 2

4. 1

5. 1

6. 3

7. 1

8. 2

9. 1

10. 2

11. 1

12. 2

13. 2

14. 1

15. 1

Practice 2

1. 오

2. 히

3. 스

4. 바

5. 조

6. 허

7. 소

8. 아

9. 저

10. 부

11. 하나

12. 자두

13. 사자

14. 오이

15. 바나나

16. 바지

17. 모자

18. 하마

19. 러브

20. 보리

Part 3

Practice 1

1. 누나

2. 거미

3. 무리

4. 다시

5. 아니

6. 하루

7. 소스

8. 두부

9. 가지

10. 소리

Practice 2

1. 우리

2. 아주

3. 누나

4. 머리

5. 우비

6. 하루

7. 사자

8. 누가

9. 그거

10. 소스

UNIT 4

Part 2

Practice 1

1. 1

2. 2

3. 2

4. 2

5. 1

6. 2

7. 1

8. 3

9. 2

10. 3

11. 3

12. 1

13. 3

14. 1

15. 2

Practice 2

1. 슈

2. 누

3. 라

4. 쥬

5. 미

6. 보

7. 거

8. 도

9. 여

10. 휴

11. 여자

12. 우유

13. 효자

14. 묘지

15. 유리

16. 보기

17. 요리

18. 소녀

19. 고려

20. 조리

Practice 3

1. 유리

2. 도구

3. 야자수

4. 바구니

5. 기러기

6. 호미

7. 지구

8. 너구리

9. 호두

10. 바다

11. 버스

12. 모기

13. 거리

14. 겨자

15. 사이다

16. 묘지

17. 두유

18. 자유

19. 교수

20. 야구

Part 3

Practice 1

1. 요리사

2. 아버지

3. 휴지

4. 주부

5. 두더지

6. 교사

7. 주사기

8. 이마

9. 교류

10. 비누

11. 모서리

12. 겨루다

13. 사파리

14. 서류

15. 여우

16. 고구마

17. 야자나무

18. 여유

19. 샤브샤브

20. 자녀

Practice 2

1. 자료

2. 이유

3. 루머

4. 뉴스

5. 미나리

6. 무료

7. 아이스

8. 거기

9. 느려요

10. 주머니

UNIT 5

Part 2

Practice 1

1. 1

2. 1

3. 1

4. 1

5. 3

6. 1

7. 2

8. 2

9. 2

10. 1

11. 3

12. 1

13. 2

14. 2

15. 1

Practice 2

1. 타

2. 츠

3. 코

4. 터

5. 치

6. 추

7. 카

8. 다

9. 파

10. 자

11. 코

12. 도

13. 보

14. 초

15. 큐

16. 듀

17. 퓨

18. 쥬

19. 교

20. 토

21. 표

22. 죠

23. 키

24. 디

25. 피

26. 지

27. 크

28. 드

29. 브

30. 츠

Practice 3

1. 가

2. 고

3. 도

4. 토

5. 바

6. 치

7. 타

8. 포

9. 치

10. 타

11. 치

12. 파

13. 파

14. 피

Practice 4

1. 차표

2. 자두

3. 표시

4. 모니터

5. 두더지

6. 파도

7. 바이러스

8. 바리스타

9. 토마토

10. 도마

11. 토스트

12. 도라지

13. 아파트

14. 규모

15. 스티커

16. 거미

17. 마스크

18. 그녀

19. 타조

20. 바다

Part 3

Practice 1

1. 커피

2. 초코

3. 튜브

4. 쿠키

5. 피자

6. 치즈

7. 도토리

8. 코트

9. 티셔츠

10. 우표

11. 카드

12. 버터

13. 토마토

14. 마스크

15. 바이러스

16. 오토바이

17. 차표

18. 치마

19. 토스트

20. 아파트

Practice 2

1. 커피

2. 튜브

3. 피자

4. 치즈

5. 도토리

6. 코트

7. 티셔츠

8. 카드

9. 토마토

10. 바이러스

11. 오토바이

12. 치마

13. 토스트

14. 바비큐

15. 마스크

UNIT 6

Part 2

Practice 1

1. 1

2. 2

3. 1

4. 2

5. 3

6. 1

7. 3

8. 1

9. 3

10. 2

11. 1

12. 3

13. 2

14. 1

15. 3

Practice 2

1. 가

2. 꼬

3. 저

4. 쟈

5. 씨

6. 죠

7. 꺼

8. 투

9. 보

10. 쳐

11. 더

12. 샤

13. 추

14. 뜨

15. 쿠

16. 버

17. 텨

18. 쓰

19. 찌

20. 커

Practice 3

1. 치

2. 지

3. 부

4. 뿌

5. 코

6. 고

7. 버

8. 빠

9. 꺄

10. 가

11. 샤, 샤

12. 쌰, 쌰

Part 3

Practice 1

1. 빠르다

2. 아빠

3. 으샤으샤

4. 주사기

5. 까치

6. 허리띠

7. 아저씨

8. 고리

9. 꼬리

10. 코리아

11. 가짜

12. 가지

13. 찌르다

14. 코끼리

15. 토키

16. 커피

17. 싸우다

18. 아보카도

19. 포도

20. 뽀뽀

Practice 2

1. 꼬리

2. 빠르다

3. 느려요

4. 두부

5. 또

6. 싸다

7. 아빠

8. 뿌리

9. 부리

10. 짜요

11. 떠요

12. 따르다

13. 도자기

14. 머리띠

15. 아저씨

UNIT 7

Part 2

Practice 1

1. 2

2. 1

3. 1

4. 2

5. 2

6. 2

7. 1

8. 2

9. 2

10. 3

11. 2

12. 1

13. 2

14. 3

15. 2

Practice 2

1. 내

2. 계

3. 매

4. 쇄

5. 과

6. 얘

7. 줘

8. 래

9. 봐

10. 케

11. 예

12. 좌

13. 걔

14. 둬

15. 뭐

16. 혜

17. 레

18. 봐

19. 얘

20. 세

Part 3

Practice 1

1. 궈 X 교과서

2. 깨 X 어깨

3. 셰 X 세수

4. 례 X 키레

5. 와 X 추워요

6. 궈 X 사과

7. 애 X 예

8. 궈 X 과자

9. 제 X 쟤

10. 졔 X 재미

11. 애 X 에쁘다

12. 계 X 게

13. 애 X 얘기

14. 게 X 기계

15. 와 X 더워요

Practice 2

1. 더워요

2. 얘기

3. 배

4. 기계

5. 얘기

6. 서예

7. 사과

8. 쟤

9. 과자

10. 추워요

11. 예쁘다

12. 카레

13. 어깨

14. 세수

15. 재미

16. 교과서

17. 게

18. 소화기

19. 타워

20. 과거

UNIT 8

Part 2

Practice 1

1. 2

2. 1

3. 2

4. 1

5. 2

6. 1

7. 2

8. 1

9. 2

10. 1

11. 2

12. 3

13. 1

14. 2

15. 2

Practice 2

1. 괴

2. 뉘

3. 희

4. 쉐

5. 의

6. 뤼

7. 죄

8. 례

9. 븨

10. 매

11. 과

12. 되

13. 휘

14. 쟤

15. 훼

16. 괴

17. 쉬

18. 붜

19. 최

20. 튀

Part 3

Practice 1

1. 궤 X 귀

2. 되 X 돼지

3. 놰 X 두뇌

4. 뉘 X 무늬

5. 킈 X 바퀴

6. 쇄 X 쉐이크

7. 위 X 스웨터

8. 웨 X 왜

9. 의 X 외로워

10. 위 X 웨이터

11. 외 X 의사

12. 웨 X 의자

13. 킈 X 퀴즈

14. 괘 X 파괴

Practice 2

1. 두뇌

2. 스웨터

3. 의자

4. 귀

5. 쉐이크

6. 의사

7. 바퀴

8. 왜

9. 퀴즈

10. 궤도

11. 돼지

12. 위로

13. 파괴

14. 외로워요

15. 추워요

16. 무늬

17. 웨이터

18. 위

19. 귀여워요

20. 뒤로

UNIT 9

Part 2

Practice 1

1. 1

2. 2

3. 2

4. 1

5. 2

6. 3

7. 3

8. 3

9. 1

10. 3

11. 2

12. 1

13. 2

14. 3

15. 1

Practice 2

1. 돌

2. 꼭

3. 벗

4. 반

5. 앞

6. 입

7. 값

8. 녕

9. 삽

10. 맥

11. 탓

12. 쌀

13. 춘

14. 덮

15. 콩

16. 엇

17. 편

18. 닭

19. 쨈

20. 깔

Practice 3

1. 4

2. 3

3. 1

4. 3

5. 3

6. 4

7. 1

8. 2

9. 1

10. 4

11. 1

12. 2

13. 2

14. 3

15. 3

Practice 4

1. 을 늘

2. 틱

3. 담

4. 일 철 을

5. 탁

6. 편

7. 낚

8. 앞 밥

9. 꽃, 있

10. 동 생 공

11. 물 을 를

12. 낮

13. 박 먹

14. 덮 들

15. 륙

Practice 5

1. ㅁ XX

2. X ㅇ

3. ㄹ ㄹ

4. X ㅅ

5. ㅅ X ㄱ

6. ㅍ X X

7. ㅊ

8. ㅆ X

9. X ㅁ ㅂ

10. X ㅍ

Practice 6

1. 섬 X 버섯

2. 얀 X 고양이

3. 갑 X 장갑

4. 늘 X 늙다

5. 탁 X 세탁기

6. 솟 X 가마솥

7. 낙 X 낚시

8. 컨 X 컴퓨터

9. 엎 X 수업

10. 꼿 X 꽃

11. 점 X 젊다

12. 릉 X 여름

13. 엄 X 굼 X 얼굴

14. 옵 X 옥수수

15. 립 X 립스틱

16. 낱 X 낮잠

17. 감 X 강아지

18. 곤 X 공부

19. 절 X 젓가락

20. 근 X 금요일

21. 봅 X 로봇

22. 잔 X 장갑

23. 빨 X 빵

24. 몹 X 목소리

25. 돈 X 동생

26. 악 X 앞치마

27. 밧 X 밖

28. 돕 X 돋보기

29. 담 X 당근

30. 응 X 가을

Practice 7

1. 할

2. 엄

3. 강

4. 업

5. 녁

6. 섯

7. 젊

8. 전

9. 발

10. 람

11. 빵

12. 륩

13. 억

14. 맛

15. 덟

16. 폰

17. 친

18. 달

19. 봄

20. 공

21. 밥

22. 학

23. 돈

24. 읽

25. 언

26. 산

27. 울

28. 힘

29. 갑

30. 꽃

Practice 8

1. 1

2. 2

3. 3

4. 2

5. 1

6. 2

7. 3

8. 1

9. 2

10. 3

11. 1

12. 3

13. 1

14. 2

15. 3

Practice 9

1. 1

2. 2

3. 2

4. 2

5. 1

6. 2

7. 2

8. 1

9. 1

10. 1

11. 2

12. 1

13. 2

14. 2

15. 1

Practice 10

1. 1

2. 1

3. 3

4. 3

5. 2

6. 1

7. 1

8. 3

9. 1

10. 2

11. 2

12. 3

13. 1

14. 3

15. 2

Part 3

Practice 3

1. 크리스틴

2. 마이클

3. 니키

4. 리사

5. 패트릭

6. 올리비아

7. 폴

8. 스테파니

9. 지미

10. 팀

Practice 4

1. 간

2. 실

3. 뻠

4. 김

5. 편

6. 동

7. 랑

8. 판

9. 점

10. 랑

11. 설

12. 몰

13. 킨

14. 악

15. 영

16. 영

17. 집

18. 악

19. 접

20. 문

21. 인

22. 절

23. 택

24. 블

25. 전

26. 장

27. 복

28. 분

29. 품

30. 망

Practice 5

1. 공

2. 산

3. 친구

4. 밥

5. 바람

6. 신발

7. 저녁

8. 옥수수

9. 버섯

10. 일요일

11. 금요일

12. 읽다

13. 젊다

14. 강아지

15. 젓가락

16. 할머니

17. 봄

18. 여름

19. 가을

20. 겨울

**CHECK UP
(UNIT 1 – UNIT 9)**

Practice 1

1. 태양

2. 스웨터

3. 일요일

4. 세수

5. 아저씨

6. 교과서

7. 세탁기

8. 의자

9. 강아지

10. 과자

11. 추워요

12. 웨이터

13. 금요일

14. 서예

15. 피자

Practice 2

1. 워싱턴 Washington

2. 로스앤젤레스 Los Angeles

3. 시애틀 Seattle

4. 애틀랜타 Atlanta

5. 샌프란시스코 San Francisco

6. 필라델피아 Philadelphia

7. 휴스턴 Houston

8. 시카고 Chicago

9. 보스턴 Boston

10. 마이애미 Miami

11. 샌디에이고 San Diego

12. 댈러스 Dallas

13. 디트로이트 Detroit

14. 덴버 Denver

15. 라스베가스 Las Vegas

Practice 3

1. 주유소

2. 예쁘다

3. 허리띠

4. 어머니

5. 티셔츠

6. 퀴즈

7. 돼지

8. 부엌

9. 젓가락

10. 버터

11. 라디오

12. 뉴스

13. 의자

14. 목소리

15. 읽다

16. 친구

17. 구름

18. 젊다

19. 꽃

20. 없다

UNIT 10

Part 1

Liaison I

1. 거부기

2. 사라믈

3. 조러븐

4. 귀거리

5. 대무느로

Liaison II

1. 찌저진

2. 다드세요

3. 보끔밥

4. 이페

5. 쪼차가다

Liaison III

1. 달마

2. 말가요

3. 발근

4. 짤바

5. 올마

Part 2

Practice 1

1. 1

2. 1

3. 2

4. 2

5. 1

6. 2

7. 1

8. 1

9. 2

10. 1

11. 1

12. 2

13. 2

14. 1

15. 1

Practice 2

1. 1

2. 1

3. 2

4. 2

5. 2

6. 1

7. 2

8. 2

9. 1

10. 1

11. 2

12. 1

13. 2

14. 1

15. 2

16. 2

17. 1

18. 1

19. 1

20. 2

Practice 3

1. 늦

2. 음

3. 름

4. 색

5. 인

6. 날

7. 을

8. 앉

9. 읽

10. 음

11. 을

12. 날

13. 됨

14. 식

15. 씹

16. 물

17. 핥

18. 옷

19. 발

20. 뜯

Part 3

Practice 1

1. 봄바람이 / 불어오네요

2. 여름은 / 아이스크림의

3. 가을에는 / 사람에게

4. 겨울에는 / 등산을

5. 낮에 / 잠을

6. 밥을 / 산책을

7. 이불을 / 덮으면

8. 옷을 / 입어야

9. 낮에 / 잠이

10. 한국음식 / 먹으러

11. 딛아야 / 인심이

12. 밖을 / 왔어요

13. 밭에는 / 수박이

14. 형님은 / 사업을

15. 한국어를 / 한국에

Practice 2

1. 거북이

2. 미국인

3. 할아버지

4. 귀걸이

5. 금요일

6. 안전운전

7. 얼음

8. 어린이

9. 닫으세요

10. 볶음밥

11. 눈높이

12. 낮에

13. 씻어

14. 있어요

15. 빛이

16. 삶은

17. 닭이

18. 읽어

19. 맑아요

20. 짧아

UNIT 11

Part 1

Tensification I - 1

1. 국쑤

2. 닫따

3. 속땀

4. 잡찌

5. 믿따

Tensification I - 2

1. 갑따

2. 뒫따리

3. 복따

4. 곧빨

5. 믿쭐

Tensification II

1. 물꼬기

2. 여름빰

3. 결씸

4. 무심껼

5. 강까

Part 2

Practice 1

1. 1

2. 2

3. 2

4. 1

5. 1

6. 2

7. 1

8. 2

9. 2

10. 2

11. 1

12. 2

13. 2

14. 1

15. 2

Practice 2

1. 2

2. 1

3. 1

4. 2

5. 1

6. 1

7. 2

8. 1

9. 1

10. 2

11. 1

12. 1

13. 2

14. 1

15. 1

16. 2

17. 1

18. 2

19. 1

20. 2

Practice 3

1. 자

2. 길

3. 갈

4. 지

5. 길

6. 시

7. 거

8. 밥

9. 증

10. 잠

11. 스

12. 동

13. 수

14. 감

15. 줄

16. 신

17. 동

18. 다

19. 감

20. 불

Part 3

Practice 1

1. 가을밤 / 숲길

2. 식당 / 덮밥

3. 늦잠 / 택시

4. 옆집 / 물고기

5. 앞발 / 닭다

6. 알맞게 / 굽다

7. 낯선 / 옥수수

8. 햇살 / 창가

9. 꽃집 / 꽃들

10. 숙제 / 낮잠

11. 찾기 / 쉽게

12. 액자 / 궁금증

13. 꽃집 / 맡고

14. 갑자기 / 각자

15. 산길 / 걷다가

Practice 2

1. 학교

2. 듣기

3. 입술

4. 국수

5. 닫다

6. 속담

7. 잡지

8. 믿다

9. 뒷다리

10. 볶다

11. 꽃밭

12. 밑줄

13. 눈사람

14. 글자

15. 비빔밥

16. 장바구니

17. 물고기

18. 여름밤

19. 강가

20. 손가락

UNIT 12

Part 1

1. 고지

2. 가치

3. 부쳐

4. 걸레바지

5. 거더부쳐

Part 2

1. 1

2. 2

3. 2

4. 1

5. 1

6. 1

7. 2

8. 1

9. 2

10. 1

11. 2

12. 1

13. 1

14. 2

15. 1

Practice 2

1. 밑

2. 맏

3. 닫

4. 샅

5. 붙

6. 받

7. 붙

8. 받

9. 돋

10. 굳

11. 끝

12. 같

13. 곧

14. 붙

15. 닫

Part 3

1. 맏이

2. 덧붙여서

3. 같이

4. 샅샅이

5. 쇠붙이

6. 여닫이

7. 굳이

8. 감쪽같이

9. 쏘아붙이면

10. 붙여야겠다

11. 곧이곧대로

12. 가을걷이

13. 피붙이

14. 낱낱이

15. 끝이

Practice 2

1. 미닫이

2. 굳이

3. 샅샅이

4. 곧이

5. 맏이

6. 같이

7. 붙여

8. 쇠붙이

9. 덧붙이다

10. 가을걷이

11. 끝이

12. 여닫이

13. 해돋이

14. 등받이

15. 피붙이

UNIT 13

Part 1

Aspirationalization I

1. 어떠케

2. 노라타

3. 까마치

4. 벌거케

5. 그러코

Aspirationalization II

1. 모타다

2. 조피다

3. 추카해

4. 바키다

5. 구치다

Part 2

Practice 1

1. 1

2. 1

3. 2

4. 1

5. 2

6. 2

7. 1

8. 2

9. 2

10. 2

11. 1

12. 2

13. 2

14. 1

15. 2

Practice 2

1. 1

2. 2

3. 2

4. 1

5. 2

6. 1

7. 2

8. 1

9. 1

10. 2

11. 1

12. 1

13. 2

14. 1

15. 1

16. 2

17. 1

18. 2

19. 2

20. 1

Practice 3

1. 복

2. 히

3. 입

4. 식

5. 형

6. 히

7. 히

8. 히

9. 게

10. 놓

11. 지

12. 다

13. 랑

14. 낳

15. 렇

16. 렇

17. 지

18. 다

19. 게

20. 득

Part 3

Practice 1

1. 울긋불긋하게

2. 급해서

3. 맺혔다

4. 그렇게

5. 노력하는

6. 입혔다

7. 막혀서

8. 잡혀서

9. 입학의

10. 잘못한

11. 정직하게

12. 밥하고

13. 잊혀지는

14. 둥그렇게

15. 닫혔다

Practice 2

1. 동그랗게

2. 그렇다

3. 놓지

4. 어떻게

5. 노랗다

6. 생각하다

7. 노력하다

8. 입학

9. 좁히다

10. 굳히다

11. 축하해

12. 잘못하다

13. 기억하다

14. 박히다

15. 잊혀지다

16. 맏형

17. 급하다

18. 식혜

19. 뿌듯하다

20. 낮 한때

UNIT 14

Part 1

Consonant Assimilation I

1. 고갱님

2. 항문

3. 낭는다

4. 방물관

5. 송마음

Consonant Assimilation II

1. 꼰눈

2. 거진말

3. 암니

4. 건모양

5. 민는다

Consonant Assimilation III

1. 궁녁

2. 층냥

3. 임녁

4. 송니산

5. 금뉴

Consonant Assimilation IV

1. 장롱

2. 종노

3. 담녁

4. 강능

5. 침냑

Consonant Assimilation V

1. 달림

2. 월리

3. 달락

4. 실랑

5. 불류

Part 2

Practice 1

1. 1

2. 1

3. 2

4. 2

5. 2

6. 1

7. 2

8. 2

9. 2

10. 2

11. 2

12. 1

13. 2

14. 1

15. 2

Practice 2

1. 1

2. 2

3. 1

4. 2

5. 2

6. 1

7. 1

8. 1

9. 2

10. 2

11. 1

12. 1

13. 2

14. 2

15. 2

16. 1

17. 1

18. 2

19. 1

20. 2

Practice 3

1. 료

2. 종

3. 막

4. 문

5. 십

6. 공

7. 한

8. 물

9. 빗

10. 압

11. 편

12. 락

13. 숙

14. 눈

15. 첫

16. 설

17. 난

18. 몽

19. 식

20. 물

Part 3

Practice 1

1. 입맛

2. 끝나무리

3. 싣는

4. 걷는다

5. 불꽃놀이

6. 이튿날

7. 연락

8. 강력하게

9. 경로당

10. 종로

11. 원리

12. 한국말

13. 감사합니다

14. 대통령

15. 오늘날

Practice 2

1. 거짓말

2. 고객님

3. 국립

4. 국물

5. 난로

6. 대통령

7. 독립

8. 박물관

9. 설날

10. 승리

11. 식물

12. 신라

13. 압력

14. 앞문

15. 연락

16. 음료수

17. 종로

18. 첫눈

19. 편리

20. 한라산

UNIT 15

Part 1

Phoneme Addition I

1. 학쌩뇽

2. 정녈

3. 부엉닐

4. 맨닙

5. 망닐

Phoneme Addition II – 1

1. 물략

2. 열료

3. 길렵

4. 솔립

5. 불려우

Phoneme Addition II – 2

1. 힘든닐

2. 할리야기

3. 겨론할려자

4. 깨끄탄뉴리

5. 쉬운녀칼

Part 2

Practice 1

1. 1

2. 1

3. 2

4. 2

5. 1

6. 1

7. 1

8. 1

9. 1

10. 2

11. 1

12. 2

13. 1

14. 2

15. 2

Practice 2

1. 1

2. 2

3. 1

4. 1

5. 2

6. 2

7. 1

8. 2

9. 1

10. 2

11. 2

12. 1

13. 2

14. 2

15. 1

16. 1

17. 1

18. 2

19. 1

20. 2

Practice 3

1. 유

2. 잎

3. 요

4. 여

5. 여

6. 연

7. 역

8. 야

9. 약

10. 일

11. 일

12. 여

13. 여

14. 일

15. 역

16. 일

17. 잎

18. 역

19. 이

20. 유

Part 3

Practice 1

1. 식용유

2. 할 일

3. 색연필

4. 태평양

5. 집안일

6. 한여름

7. 맨입

8. 길옆

9. 힘든 일

10. 열여섯

11. 맛있는

12. 퍼질 이야기

13. 무슨 일

14. 쉬운 역할

15. 풀잎

Practice 2

1. 깨진 유리

2. 꽃잎

3. 단풍잎

4. 담요

5. 더운 여름

6. 맛있는 요리

7. 배낭여행

8. 서울역

9. 식용유

10. 신나는 야구

11. 알약

12. 연료

13. 예쁜 여자

14. 올여름

15. 정열

16. 지하철역

17. 태평양

18. 풀잎

19. 한여름

20. 휘발유

UNIT 16

Part 1

Sai-sori Phenomenon I

1. 찰짠

2. 기찰낄

3. 나묻까지

4. 전볻때

5. 빋빵울

Sai-sori Phenomenon II

1. 훈날

2. 바단물

3. 콘날

4. 진딘물

5. 왼눈썹

Sai-sori phenomenon III

1. 배춘닙

2. 담밴닙

3. 베갠닏

4. 옌닐

5. 뒨님맏

Part 2

Practice 1

1. 1

2. 1

3. 1

4. 2

5. 1

6. 1

7. 1

8. 2

9. 1

10. 2

11. 1

12. 2

13. 1

14. 2

15. 1

Practice 2

1. 1

2. 2

3. 1

4. 2

5. 1

6. 2

7. 1

8. 1

9. 1

10. 2

11. 2

12. 2

13. 1

14. 1

15. 2

16. 2

17. 1

18. 2

19. 2

20. 1

Practice 3

1. 댓

2. 잇

3. 날

4. 일

5. 랫

6. 뭇

7. 물

8. 볕

9. 닷

10. 빗

11. 방

12. 잔

13. 훗

14. 윗

15. 춧

16. 염

17. 물

18. 길

19. 대

20. 잣

Part 3

Practice 1

1. 뒷입맛

2. 베갯잇

3. 배춧잎

4. 아랫입술

5. 시쳇말

6. 옛날

7. 수돗물

8. 윗눈썹

9. 혼잣말

10. 세숫물

11. 뒷발차기

12. 진딧물

13. 잔칫상

14. 혓바늘

15. 고깃국

Practice 2

1. 깻잎

2. 나뭇가지

3. 노랫말

4. 뒷문

5. 비닷가

6. 바닷물

7. 배춧잎

8. 빗물

9. 빗방울

10. 빗소리

11. 수돗물

12. 옛날

13. 윗입술

14. 이삿짐

15. 잇몸

16. 전봇대

17. 존댓말

18. 찻잔

19. 촛불

20. 혼잣말

FINAL CHECK UP (UNIT 1 – UNIT 16)

Practice 2

1. 콩

2. 때우다

3. 자다

4. 뿔

5. 시름

6. 탈

7. 뽀송뽀송

8. 가지

9. 탱글탱글

10. 쭈글쭈글

11. 뿌리

12. 장구

13. 빨강

MORE BOOKS BY LINGO MASTERY

We are not done teaching you Korean until you're fluent!

Here are some other titles you might find useful in your journey of mastering Korean:

✓ Korean Short Stories for Beginners

✓ Intermediate Korean Short Stories

✓ 2000 Most Common Korean Words in Context

✓ Conversational Korean Dialogues

But we got many more!

Check out all of our titles at **www.LingoMastery.com/korean**